Choices
A Guide for Young People

Gill Gordon

Illustrations by Petra Röhr-Rouendaal

MACMILLAN

TALC

DFID

First published 1999 by
MACMILLAN EDUCATION LTD
London and Oxford
Companies and representatives throughout the world

www.macmillan-africa.com

ISBN 0-333-68746-9

9	8	7	6	5	4	3	2
08	07	06	05	04	03	02	01

This book is printed on paper suitable for recycling and
made from fully managed and sustained forest sources.

Printed in Malaysia

A catalogue record for this book is available from the
British Library.

Illistrations (including cover) by Petra Röhr-Rouendall

Contents

Acknowledgements

The source of inspiration for this book comes from the young people in Nigeria, Ghana, The Gambia, Zambia, Kenya and Uganda who talked about their vision of an ideal sexual relationship of companionship, trust and love and how they might reach it. Their optimism and determination to reach their goals in spite of formidable obstacles was humbling. I wish to thank all those young people whose ideas form the basis of this book.

This book also owes a debt of gratitude to the colleagues who have shared ideas and learning activities in the area of sexual and reproductive health, adolescence, girl's empowerment and human interaction. Ideas and activities have been adapted from the following excellent written sources:

Burns, A. et al (1997) *Where Women Have No Doctor. A health guide for women*, Hesperian Foundation

The Clarity Collective (1989) *Taught Not Caught: strategies for sex education*, Learning Development Aids

Dixon, H., Gordon, P. (1990) *Working with Uncertainty. A handbook for those involved in training on HIV and AIDS*, FPA

Fine, F. (1992) *Playing with Fire. Training for the creative use of conflict*, The Leaveners (Quaker Arts Projects)

Hampton, J. (1987) *Healthy Living, Healthy Loving*, Macmillan Publishers

Joinet, B. and Mugolola, T. (1995) *The Fleet of Hope.* PO Box 9330, Dar es Salaam, Tanzania

Lynch, E. (1991) *Unmasking AIDS and Activities to Explore*, IPPF

Perlman, H. (Editor for UPBEAT and PPASA) *Bodywise. Sex Education, Health and Advice for South African Youth*, Sached Books

Promoting positive mental health. Resource pack, (1996) Health Promotion Unit for Brighton, Hove and Lewes

Szirom T. and Dyson, S. (1990) *Greater Expectations: a source book for working with girls and young women*, Learning Development Aids

Welbourne, A. (1995) *Stepping Stones. A training package on HIV/AIDS, communication and relationship skills*, Strategies for Hope

Petra Röhr-Rouendaal has made the book exciting with illustrations that bring the ideas to life and provide many positive role models. Her constant encouragement and creativity during the production of this book has been a source of energy and inspiration.

I wish to express my appreciation to those who took the time to read the manuscript and give me feedback on how to improve it. My thanks to my husband, Njoroge, for his suggestions and for always keeping me in touch with reality. My children, Jon and Vanessa, and a friend Katy read some of the chapters and encouraged me to go on. Clement Sakala, the IEC Programme Officer for the Planned Parenthood Association of Zambia and the PPAZ youth group (Mwangana Frank, Phiri Zikhalo, Leah Zulu, Fisonga Mulunda, Mwale Vincent, Sunga Sakala, Malama Edward and Banda Mulilanji) in Chipata, Eastern Province, Zambia gave me feedback and inspiration from the start. Zimanele Magagula commented on the manuscript from Swaziland. Peer motivators from the Planned Parenthood Association of Ghana/Population Concern Project in Akuapem gave feedback on the illustrations.

Special thanks go to Rachel Carnegie, who had faith in my vision of the book and encouraged me to write it initially. Her detailed comments, insights and suggestions were very helpful. Thanks also to June Copeland and Indira Benbow for their comments and suggestions. I appreciate the support of Professor David Morley in commenting on the manuscript and seeking funding.

I am deeply indebted to Dr Florence Manguyu, who has just completed a term as Honorary President of the Medical Women's International Association, for her thoughtful comments and the Foreword, which sets the scene for the reader with great insight into the needs of African young people.

I have greatly appreciated my relationship with Shirley Hamber, my editor. Her belief in the book, perseverance, helpful comments and friendly pushing kept me moving on the manuscript when the trials of the life of a freelance consultant threatened to overwhelm me.

Finally, I wish to thank the Department For International Development (DFID) and the Tudor Trust for their generous grants, which have enabled us to produce this book at low cost so that it can reach those who do not normally have access to books.

Foreword

Choices comes at a very appropriate time when the world is being made aware of the needs of young people. This awareness was created following the UN International Conference on Population and Development, (ICPD) in Cairo, 1994 and the Fourth World Conference on Women, (FWCW) in Beijing, 1995.

Young people between the ages of 15 and 24 comprise about 20 per cent of the world's population of about 1.2 billion. This book addresses the needs of even younger people and hence an even bigger group of the population. Young people are not just an important sector of the population, they are the most important. We are currently witnessing the largest generation of young people the world has ever had. These young people are endowed with great potential and in order to fully exploit this potential they need good nutrition and quality health care, education and accurate information, employment and services for their needs especially in reproductive health. Young people have the right and an important role to play in the sustainable development of the world. But for every right there is a responsibility.

Gill Gordon, in this book, has given the youth, their parents and guardians, their teachers and counsellors, the basic information that young people so badly need as they face the challenges brought about by our fast moving world. When societies develop fast, age old human values and social support systems are often lost as people adopt new ideas for which they are ill prepared. Gill Gordon bridges this transition by providing the information required. This book gives the basics on which ideas can be developed and strengthened to suit the particular situation. Life is precious, we therefore need to respect and treasure not just our own, but other people's lives as well.

We may not know what the next millennium has for us but through this book, Gill Gordon shows us how we can prepare the youth, our future, for the next century. Many people are bewildered and often ask 'where is the youth of today heading to?'. We would be wiser asking 'Where is the youth of today coming from?' This book, in a very candid manner, provides adults and young people with the life principles and tools needed to face the future. *Choices* should form the basis for any credible reproductive health education for young people if indeed the world is serious about the future. This responsibility is not in the hands of young people alone, but collectively in their families and the wider society.

Dr Florence W. Manguyu, Nairobi, Kenya.

Dr Florence Manguyu is a Kenyan paediatrician in clinical practice in Nairobi. She has just completed a term as Honorary President of the Medical Women's International Association. She is a member of the WHO Global Commission on Women's Health and was a member of the international NGO planning committee for the Cairo Conference (ICPD).

Introduction

Who is this book for and how can you use it?

Choices is written for young people aged between 10 and
24 years; for peer educators and youth leaders; for teachers,
health workers and parents and anyone who is helping young
people to grow up as fulfilled and responsible human beings with
a sexual and social life.

Young people can read the book for themselves and share it with
their friends. They can try out the activities with friends and family.
They might get help from peer educators, teachers or youth
leaders to do the activities with a group of peers.

Peer educators, youth leaders or teachers can use *Choices* to
organise learning sessions. The guide at the back of the book
explains how to do the different activities. If they are new, try
them out with some colleagues.

It is important to select the information and activities that are
appropriate for the age, lifestyle and needs of the group. However,
adults often make assumptions that young people are too young
to talk about and worry about sex. Our own embarrassment with
the topic can get in the way of giving young people the
information that they need.

Adapt the activities, pictures, cartoons and quizzes for different
groups.

Parents of adolescents might read sections of the book together
with their children and discuss the issues. This will help parents
and adolescents to communicate more easily.

What is the purpose of the book and what does it contain?

The book aims to:

- provide accurate information on sexual and reproductive health;
- suggest activities aimed at exploring values and attitudes in
  relation to culture and the changing world; and building
  self-esteem;

- suggest activities aimed at practising skills in communication, assertiveness, risk avoidance, problem-solving, decision-making and advocacy.

Chapter 1 describes how culture influences our lives and how societies adapt it to changing situations. Chapter 2 covers the physical, emotional and social changes that happen during puberty. The importance of self-esteem, communication skills, assertiveness, responsibility, good decision-making and self-respect are explored in Chapter 3. Chapter 4 looks at relationships and the importance of young men and women making good decisions about sex. Sexual pleasure is seen as a right for men and women and a way of enhancing marital relations. Chapter 5 deals with rape and sexual abuse and suggests ways to prevent them and to help those who have suffered from them. In Chapter 6, the book outlines how people can have 'children by choice, not chance' so that mothers, fathers and children lead healthy and happy lives. Chapter 7 addresses the prevention and treatment of STDs and HIV/AIDS. Chapter 8 discusses the importance of eating nutritious foods, taking enough rest and exercise, reducing stress and avoiding alcohol, tobacco and other drugs. In Chapter 9 readers are invited to share their hopes and plans for linking hands with families, friends and neighbours, health workers and teachers, churches and mosques to make everyone's lives happier and safer.

What is the impact of sex education?

Many people worry that giving young people information about sex will push them into early sexual activity and promiscuity. However, a review by WHO of many studies around the world has shown that good sex education results in a delay in sexual activity and increased safer sex practice when sex does start.

Points of view

'I was not told anything about sex when I was growing up – my parents just said that I should not play with boys after I started my periods. When I fell in love, I just did what came naturally. I had no idea that I could get pregnant the first time nor that he would walk out on me. I always answer my children's questions honestly and encourage them to talk to me about their friendships.'

'We boys learnt about sex from each other. We thought that we should start having sex early otherwise our organs would shrivel and our future wives laugh at us. I did not want a girl friend and I was worried about diseases, but I got drunk and tried to catch one. Then a health worker taught us about sex. He said that waiting for sex until you are mature and find someone that you really care about is a good choice, not a failure as a man. That made me feel so good – I stopped worrying about sex and concentrated on my studies. I had the facts I needed for the right time and I learnt to respect myself and girls enough to wait for the right one.'

'I am a teacher. At first I thought why should I teach these children about sex – an adult matter – they will only be worried or embarrassed or start to do it. Then I overheard some children talking about how they watched their parents in bed and were planning to try it themselves. They had the information all wrong and I thought, with this AIDS around, I am putting their lives at risk by keeping quiet. Now I teach them about sexuality and answer all their questions. But I tell them this:

'You probably will not need this knowledge and these skills for some years yet. You may never meet some of the problems that you learn about. But when you have the knowledge and the skills and you value yourself, you will be prepared to make good decisions when the time comes. It is easier to think about these things calmly when you are not involved in a sexual relationship.

And remember, sex is not a game. It can give great pleasure and happiness if it is done with care and love. But it is also risky because there is no 100 per cent protection against pregnancy, STD/HIV and emotional hurt. So treat sex, yourself and your friends with respect.'

What do you think?

Sexuality is an area of life that arouses strong emotions because it is closely linked to our personal and cultural values. This book includes activities and ideas that people in some cultures disapprove of and others find acceptable or good. The author has her own sexual values. Africa contains many different sexual cultures and it is not possible to write a book that will please everyone. Sections that address sexual behaviour aim to provide comprehensive and accurate information and give readers an opportunity to explore the advantages and disadvantages of these behaviours for themselves. The book is not promoting one sexual choice over others but rather giving readers the full range of choices, from abstinence to safe sex.

For example, some cultures strongly disapprove of masturbation. This is a value that they hold. However, sexual therapists and people from other cultures view masturbation as a natural and positive expression of sexuality that can help people to practise safer sex and enjoy sex more with their partners. This book aims to give people new perspectives to consider for themselves.

The book promotes the following values:

- People have the right to express their sexuality in ways that do not harm other people.
- Men and women should jointly decide on sexual activity.
- Everyone has the right to refuse sexual activity at any time, with any partner.
- Everyone has the right to sexual pleasure.
- Sex is best expressed in a loving, caring relationship.
- It is necessary to be open and honest about the reality of young people's sexual lives and the factors influencing them, in order to help them to be safe and happy.

1 The world is changing

This book is about change. It is about change in our bodies and minds as we grow older; and change in our societies and the world. We may find change exciting and good or scary and painful. Sometimes we can influence changes in our lives and sometimes we have no control over them. However, the more we understand what is happening to us and why, the more we are able to influence and cope with change. It helps if we have confidence in ourselves, our culture and the people who support us; if we can explore the good and bad points in our lives and work to bring about good changes. Our family, friends and community may help us to do this or they may make it difficult.

Over the past ten years, three big international meetings have made global agreements saying that:

- women should have the right to make their own decisions about marriage, sexual activity and child-bearing;
- there should be equal and respectful relationships between men and women;
- young people have the right to information and services about the sexual side of life and should make their own decisions about marriage and sexual activity;
- children and young people have the right to participate in decisions affecting their lives, to freedom of expression and access to information and education; they have a right to survival, proper development and protection from abuse and exploitation.

This book aims to help parents, teachers and young people to make these rights a reality. It provides information on sexual and reproductive health and encourages discussion between young and old, boys and girls, men and women.

The book focuses on young people, and girls in particular, for several reasons. Young people often find it difficult to earn a living and improve their lives. Girls are usually at more of a disadvantage and have lower status than boys. They are expected to be submissive and do less well in school and work. Fewer girls go to school and stay in school than boys and they often have less time to study. A girl's reproductive system and lower status make her more likely to suffer from sexual and reproductive health problems. Girls have fewer ways to earn money and may be pushed into sexual relationships for money. All these disadvantages have a huge cost for the well-being of girls and women, and the whole society.

The empowerment of girls can open the doors to progress in African communities. Empowerment means:

- improving women's ability to make decisions based on their own and others' needs;
- enabling women to control resources such as money, time and their own bodies;
- girls having power within themselves to challenge the rules that give them low status, to look at their situation and find solutions;
- instead of individuals feeling 'I cannot', the group feels 'we can'.

Communities are more progressive places when the women can read and write; when the talents of women are used in decision-making and creative, family and economic work. In communities where women and men can talk and love as equals, women are less likely to bear too many children and die early in childbirth or from HIV. Everyone – women, children and men – has a better life.

This chapter explores the idea of culture and introduces some parts of culture that affect young people. It argues that culture is a living thing, not a fossil to cling to and hide behind. It looks at how changes in gender, sexuality and reproduction, education and work could result in the empowerment of girls and progress in society.

What is culture?

Culture describes what we think, learn and do as individuals and what our society considers important. Culture reflects our history and tradition; it is based on our social, economic and environmental situation. Culture provides guidelines on how we should meet our needs for food, shelter, clothing; and how we should raise children. It gives us our basic religious and social values.

Culture is constantly changing, for good or ill. Like a living tree, it has roots in the soil and leaves and fruits that constantly renew themselves. The roots give us tradition and the leaves and fruits allow us to develop our values based on influences within and outside our society.

When we listen to ideas, we decide if they are good or bad. We can do this with our own culture. Cultural practices can have good or bad effects on different people in the community. Our history can often give good reasons for a particular practice. But the world may have changed and the bad effects of the practice may outweigh the good. We may need a new practice.

All societies change to take account of new know-ledge and situations. Young people often have cultural differences from their parents and grand-parents. This can lead to quarrels. New ideas travel around the world fast through global institutions, media and travel. The exchange of ideas between cultures can be enriching and give opportunities for improving our lives. We need to combine the best of the old and the new and let go of ideas that are no longer helpful.

Huphuet Boigny, President of Côte d'Ivoire, said 'we should see culture as a river leading us forward, not a stagnant pool where we stay in one place. Culture is a guide that enables us to progress, not a heavy weight that holds us back'.

Activities

1 Discuss President Boigny's statement. How does it apply to your own culture?

2 Ask your grandparents what has changed from the time they were children of your age until now. Which changes do they think have made life better and which ones have made it worse?

3 Choose a tradition from your own culture. Make a picture to show the good and bad points about it. How could you keep the best things about it, whilst leaving behind the bad points?

4 Think of some new ideas from outside your own culture. Discuss which ideas are good and which ideas are harmful. For example, some videos show sex without respect or love. They show the worst of world culture. Some videos show loving relationships between men and women or parents and children and could act as role models.

This book helps you to look at both your own and outside cultures to decide what is good for you. We ask you to think about why the characters in the book think and behave as they do and make up your own mind. This will help you to make good decisions when you come across similar situations and feel confident about your own values.

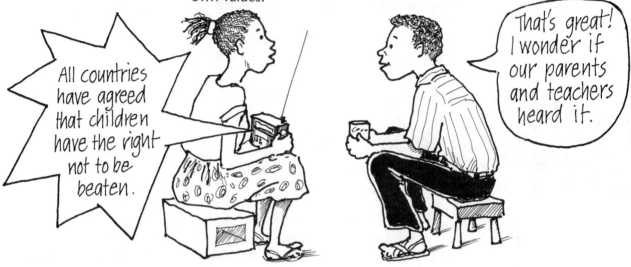

All countries have agreed that children have the right not to be beaten.

That's great! I wonder if our parents and teachers heard it.

Ellen and Joshua's story

Ellen and Joshua were born in a village. Ellen attended an initiation camp when she was twelve years old and learnt how to be a good wife. She was betrothed to marry when she was fifteen. Then their father got a job in the city and the family moved. Joshua and Ellen went to school. They enjoyed hearing about new ideas from their friends and lessons. Every Saturday the children watched videos. They liked the way the men and women talked easily to each other and fell in love. Children said what they thought to adults and no-one was beaten. The young people copied the language they heard on the videos. They bought jeans and Ellen enjoyed the freedom of these clothes; they made her feel strong. She enjoyed the clubs where she could debate with the boys. In the city she saw women working as drivers and men as cooks.

In the holidays, Ellen and Joshua returned to their village to stay with their uncle. Ellen was introduced to her future husband. He was old and he already had a wife. She did not love him. Her uncle shouted at her for wearing jeans and ripped them to pieces. He said that she was a prostitute because she talked so freely with the boys and did not show respect. The boys laughed at Joshua when he helped Ellen to fetch water and firewood. The young people who had stayed outside the village met together by the river. They talked about how they were the new generation and they would live their lives in a different way from their parents …

1 Discuss the story.

- Why did Ellen and Joshua see things in a different way from some of the people in their village?

- What are the good and bad things about the ideas of the 'new generation'?

- How can young and older people talk together about their different ideas in a more helpful way?

2 Read out the statements below one by one.

- Marriages arranged by the family work better than love marriages chosen by young people.

- Children should be seen and not heard.

- A girl who dresses in jeans is a prostitute.

- Boys who cook and fetch water are weak.

Decide whether you agree or disagree with these statements. In pairs, take it in turns to explain why you agree or disagree. Listen carefully to each other and try to understand.

We will now explore how cultural change can empower young people, especially girls, and bring progress to the whole society. We begin by looking at the social differences between males and females.

What do we mean by sex and gender?

Sex is biological and genetic. It describes our physical bodies: we are female if we have a vagina and breasts; we are male if we have a penis and testicles.

Gender is created by each society. Gender describes how girls and boys, men and women, and all groups in society should behave. Gender differs from community to community.

Society tells us what roles, activities and responsibilities are right for males and females of different ages and how they should behave towards each other. It lays down the status of men and women and who has more power. These ways of behaving are seen as 'natural', a fixed part of culture, even by women who are disadvantaged by them. This hinders change. However they can change with new ideas and new situations.

The following activities help you think about how gender affects your life and how you might like things to change.

● Activities

1 Think of proverbs, songs and stories that tell how a girl or woman and a boy or man should behave in your society.

2 Draw pictures/cartoons or do some role plays to show the answer to these questions in your culture:

- How is a 'good' girl or young woman expected to behave?
- How is a 'good' boy or young man expected to behave?
- How do these expectations affect your life? Which ones have a good effect and which ones have a bad effect on your life?

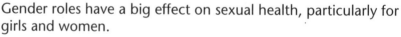

Gender roles have a big effect on sexual health, particularly for girls and women.

What is sexual and reproductive health?

Several chapters of this book are about sexual and reproductive health. This is our physical, mental, social and spiritual well-being in the part of our lives to do with being a man or a woman. It includes our sexual relationships, getting married, having children, protecting ourselves from infection and making choices. This is a very important part of our lives but one that we often believe we should not talk about. This lack of communication between adults and young people, men and women, results in many problems, especially for women. Without good information, confidence and power, girls may die from AIDS or unsafe abortion. They may suffer infertility or unwanted pregnancy, resulting in poverty and isolation. Girls and boys have a right to information about their changing bodies. They also have a right to opportunities to explore their values and gain skills and self-esteem that will help them to grow up safe and happy as human beings with a sexual and social life.

● Activities

1 Draw pictures or do role plays to show your vision of good sexual and reproductive health. Keep this vision in your mind as you read this book. Add to it new pictures and the steps that you will take to reach your dream.

2 Divide into two boys' groups and two girls' groups. One of each makes separate lists of the rights that girls and boys have over their sexual lives. The other two groups make separate lists of the responsibilities of boys and girls in their sexual lives. Put the lists up and add new ideas. What are the similarities and differences between the male and female lists? How do these apply to your own lives?

Learning and education are key areas of our culture that have a major impact on our lives.

Learning for life

We learn new things throughout our lives, as small children at home, through our years at school or work until the day we die. The knowledge and skills we gain from home and experience are as valuable as knowledge we gain from books.

Activity

Think of the knowledge, values and skills that you have learnt from:

- family
- community
- friends
- school
- media (books, radio, drama, television).

Why is it important to go to school?

The ability to read and write enables us to understand information in forms, newspapers, posters and books. We learn about new ideas from our own country and the world. We can better understand politics and economics and use services more effectively. Science helps us to understand how our bodies work and how to stay healthy. Education opens up new work opportunities for boys and girls.

Activity

There is a saying, 'If you educate a boy, you educate an individual. If you educate a girl, you educate a nation'.

Why do you think they say this? Do you agree?

It has been shown that mothers who have been to school have healthier children. They take good care of their children and use the health services when the child is sick.

We can see that it is important for girls to go to school, so let's explore the reasons why girls find it more difficult than boys to attend school, stay in school and perform well.

Activity

Draw a picture or make a role play to show all the reasons why fewer girls go to school and stay in school than boys in your community.

Amina's story

'I was the best girl in my class. I wanted to be a doctor. But my mother could not pay my fees, she only had enough for my brother. Now I am to be married to a man in my village next month when I am 14 years old. I hope that this does not happen to any of my friends, because if you are married, you have nothing to do again but sit at home'.

The men and women in Amina's village met to see why girls do not go to school and what they could do to help them. These pictures show why girls did not go to school, stay in school and do well.

Kane, E. (1993)
Groundwork: Participatory research for girl's education.
Manual and video.
EDIHR/ASTHR, The World Bank, Washington, D.C.

Some girls did not do as well as boys because they were expected to do a lot of housework and garden work at the busiest time of the school year.

How can communities help their girls to go to school?

In The Gambia, the community made a plan to help their girls to go to school. Some of their ideas were:

- to get money for fees by increasing mothers' income through gardening; collecting money from each household; and giving 50 per cent of the money from women's and men's savings groups to educate girls;
- to educate parents on the benefits of education and discourage early marriage;
- to give boys and girls 'family life education' and to have parents supervising evening classes for girls and boys;
- to encourage girls to stay in school so that they can train as teachers.

Find out about literacy classes in your community. Get together and see whether you could help young people who cannot read and write to form a regular group for literacy classes.

In many communities, children start to work in the family home or farm from an early age. The type and amount of work we do has a major impact on our well-being.

The world of work

We work to feed, clothe and house ourselves, to keep healthy and raise our children. We also work to earn money or produce food or resources. Both of these types of work are essential for our survival and fulfilment. Women are expected to do some tasks and men are expected to do others. Women often do the tasks that keep the home going **and** earn money or produce food. Men do the tasks that earn money or grow food. This often means that women work for longer hours than men.

How do we earn money and how do we spend it?

Many young men and women find ways to earn some money whilst they are still at school or when they have left school.

● Activities

1 Draw an income (money earned) and expenditure (money spent) tree for girls and boys. The roots show all the ways that girls or boys can earn some money. The leaves show the different items that boys or girls spend money on.

2 Put the trees up on the wall and compare them. What can we learn from the trees? What are the good and bad things about the sources of income and the ways girls and boys use money?

3 Now imagine that you are 25 years old. Draw an income and expenditure tree to show all the possible sources of income for women and men at that age. What expenses are women and men likely to have?

4 Are sources of income different for males and females? Why is that? Are there some jobs that only men can do and some that only women can do?

What do you want to do when you grow up?

Young people often have different expectations for the future from their parents. In the past, girls may have seen themselves as wives, mothers and farmers. Now they may see themselves as seamstresses, drivers, traders, doctors, teachers or MPs.

● Activities

Try it for yourself.

1 In single sex groups, write, draw or use a symbol to show different ways of earning a living down one side of a square on the ground or on a piece of paper. Put the factors that you will think about when you decide what work to do across the top.

2 Make notes on or score each job according to the different factors. This will help you to think about what type of work you could do now and what work you might like to do later.

JOB	INCOME	ENJOY	MY TALENT	HEALTH + SAFETY	COST OF STARTING	ABLE TO HAVE CHILDREN AROUND
TRADING	●●	●	●●	●	●●	●●
HAIRDRESSING	●●●	●●●		●●	●●	●●●
FOOD PROCESSING						
SEAMSTRESS	●●●	●●●●	?	●●●	●	●●●
FARMER	●	●	●●●●	●	●●●●	●
CIVIL SERVANT						
TEACHER						
NURSE						
DOCTOR						
DRIVER						

The actions that we take at different stages of our lives and the way that we behave sets us on one path or another. It is helpful to think about the underlying reasons why we behave as we do.

Why do we behave as we do?

Health educators often give people messages about what they should and should not do. This is especially true with sex education for young people. But the way we all behave is influenced by forces at a personal, family, community, national and international level. None of us are free agents. The more we understand and are able to control the forces that affect our health, the more we are able to live active, fulfilled lives.

Our knowledge, attitudes, skills, support from others, environment and how much money and power we have affect our behaviour.

2 | Growing up

Physical, emotional, spiritual and social changes at puberty

When boys and girls reach 10 or 11, their bodies start to change from the body of a child to the body of an adult. This change is called **puberty**. It happens between the ages of about 10 and 18 years. Puberty is the start of the period we call **adolescence**.

Chemicals in the body called hormones start the changes at puberty. These hormones make the body produce the eggs and sperm that can make a baby.

What are the changes at puberty?

Boys

Height increases suddenly.

Get pimples. Glands called sebaceous glands produce too much oil.

Moustache and beard start to grow. Voice gets deeper. For a while voice is squeaky (voice 'breaks').

Shoulders and chest get broader.

Hair starts to grow under arms.

Pubic hair starts to grow.

Penis and testes get bigger. Male sex cells, called sperm, start being produced in the testes.

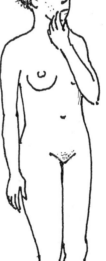

Girls

Girls are often taller than boys.

Get pimples.

Hair starts to grow under arms.

Breasts develop.

Pubic hair starts to grow.

The ovaries get bigger and develop. Female sex cells, called ova, or egg cells, develop in the ovaries. Periods usually start about a year after breasts develop.

At puberty, the sweat glands in boys and girls produce a scent, which is attractive to the opposite sex. They begin to admire each other, have romantic feelings and feel moody.

Everyone grows and has body changes at different rates, so do not worry if your friends change faster or more slowly than you. By the age of 18, everyone will look like a young man or women rather than a boy or girl. If you are worried about your growth, see a doctor.

During adolescence boys and girls become more independent and may want to set up their own homes. They take more care over clothes and cosmetics. Some become more religious whilst others may explore new values outside formal religion.

What can girls and boys do about pimples?

Pimples will go away when the glands have settled down. In the meantime, reduce pimples in these ways:

- Wash your face with soap and water several times a day.
- Eat lots of fruit and vegetables and not too much fatty food like chocolate and fried foods.
- Drink lots of water.
- Do not pick pimples because this can lead to infection and scars.
- Get some cream from the health worker or chemist if the spots are very bad.
  - Do not use skin lightening creams because they contain a poison that damages skin so that it comes out in dark patches and lumps.

They say this cream makes you light and beautiful.

I think black is beautiful. Why do you want to be white?

How do girls develop?

Boys and girls have sex organs that make up the reproductive system. This system makes babies.

Girls have some sex organs outside their bodies and some inside. Some girls feel shy about their sex organs because they have been told that they are dirty and ugly and they should not touch them. But all parts of the body are beautiful and clean if they are washed every day!

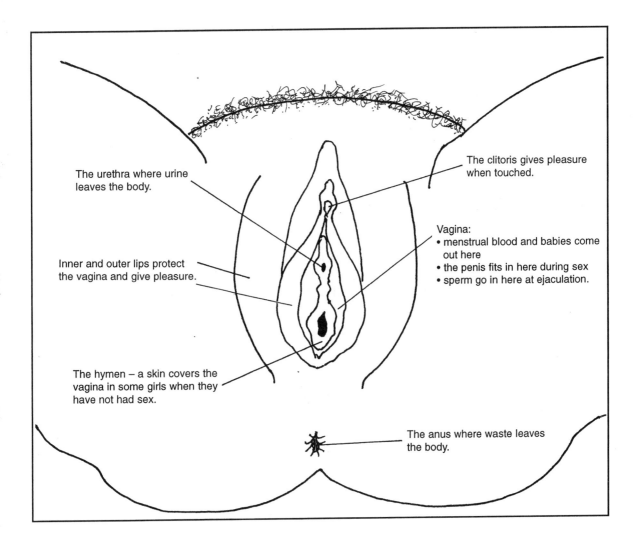

The urethra where urine leaves the body.

The clitoris gives pleasure when touched.

Inner and outer lips protect the vagina and give pleasure.

Vagina:
• menstrual blood and babies come out here
• the penis fits in here during sex
• sperm go in here at ejaculation.

The hymen – a skin covers the vagina in some girls when they have not had sex.

The anus where waste leaves the body.

The vagina is a wonderful organ

- The walls of the vagina are made of muscles that women can squeeze to make sex more enjoyable and keep fit for childbirth. They can practise this without anyone knowing! They imagine that they want to stop in the middle of urinating; those are the muscles to squeeze.

- The walls of the vagina produce some fluid that keeps the vagina clean. This is normal and good; do not wash it out with water or soap.

The amount and type of fluid changes during the menstrual cycle. When the egg is released from the ovary, the fluid is stretchy like egg white. This is a sign that a girl could become pregnant if she has sex.

When a girl is sexually excited, the vagina makes more fluid. Girls may notice this happening when they think about sexy things or have nice dreams about sex. The liquid makes sex comfortable and prevents sores.

If the fluid is smelly or you have itching or pain, go to a clinic or health worker at once. You may have an infection that needs treatment so that it does not damage your organs. See page 86.

- The vagina grows and stretches during puberty. The walls of the vagina and mouth of the womb are not fully-grown until girls are about 18 years old. This makes it easier for germs to enter the reproductive organs of girls under the age of 18 years and damage them. They are also more easily damaged by childbirth.

- There is a place inside the vagina, towards the front of the body, called the 'G' spot that gives women sexual pleasure when it is touched. This is different from the clitoris, which is outside the body.

If a girl has not yet had sex, a thin skin called the hymen sometimes covers the vagina. In some cultures, people say that a girl without a hymen is not a virgin. This is not true. Some girls are born with very thin hymens and they are easily broken by exercise or using tampons.

Girls should always wipe themselves from front to back when they clean themselves after the toilet to prevent germs from the anus going into the vagina or urine tube and causing infections.

What are the sex organs inside the body?

The **cervix** is the door to the womb. It is a very small opening and nothing can get through except sperm, germs and menstrual blood. The cervix opens during childbirth so that the baby can get out. A doctor can make the opening bigger with an instrument if needed, for example, to insert a contraceptive called an IUCD.

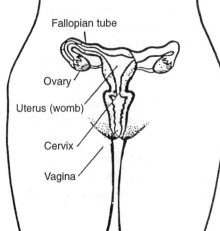

Fallopian tube

Ovary

Uterus (womb)

Cervix

Vagina

The **uterus** or womb is where the baby lives for nine months before it is born. The womb is made of muscle that works hard during childbirth to open the cervix.

The two **ovaries** take it in turns to release a tiny egg each month that can join with a sperm to make a baby. Sometimes eggs are released from both ovaries together; if they are both fertilised, the woman will have twins. Girls are born with thousands of eggs, to last them until the menopause when they stop releasing eggs.

The **Fallopian tubes** lead from the ovary to the womb. The egg travels along the tube to the womb every month. If a girl has a serious Sexually Transmitted Disease (STD) which is not treated, the tubes can become blocked. Then the egg cannot reach the womb and the girl cannot become pregnant.

What are periods?

Many girls begin to have periods when they are about 11 years old but this can happen between the ages of 9 and 18. Periods often start about a year after breasts appear. Many girls have no warning and they are surprised to find some blood between their legs. If no one has told them about periods this can be frightening. Periods are not dirty or dangerous; they are a natural sign that a girl is becoming a woman and can become pregnant.

A girl can become pregnant before her periods start because she releases an egg before her first period.

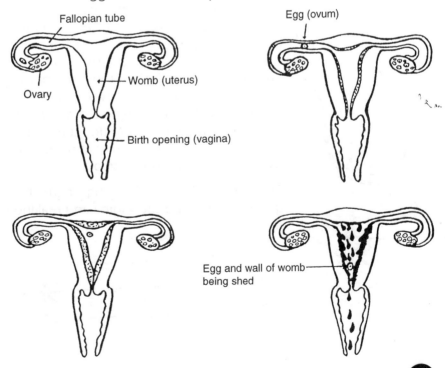

Fallopian tube

Egg (ovum)

Ovary

Womb (uterus)

Birth opening (vagina)

Egg and wall of womb being shed

Every month the body prepares a rich lining in the womb, like a soft nest, in case the woman becomes pregnant. Every month the ovary releases an egg that travels down the Fallopian tube to the womb. Usually the egg is not needed and it dies. The rich lining of the womb breaks down and leaves the body through the vagina. This is called menstruation.

If a female and male have sex at the time the egg is released, without using a contraceptive, the sperm and egg may join to make a baby. The baby will plant itself in the lining of the womb and start to grow. Then menstruation stops. This is the first sign of pregnancy.

Many women have a period every 28 days. Some have them every 21 days and some every 35 days. Periods usually last about 4 days, but they can be shorter or longer.

Many adolescent girls have irregular and sometimes painful periods. They settle down as girls grow up.

Keeping clean during periods

Girls can use sanitary towels, tampons, cotton wool or pieces of cloth to catch the blood during their periods.

Sanitary towels are worn outside between the legs. Girls should change the towel every few hours so that the blood does not smell or grow germs.

Tampons are put inside the vagina with a string hanging out. Cotton wool is also used. They soak up the blood inside and so do not smell. Girls **must** change the tampon or cotton wool at least every eight hours and make sure that they have removed the used one. If tampons are left in too long they can grow germs that can make girls very sick. It is very important to remove the last tampon or cotton wool when the period has finished. If you have a high fever, rash, fainting or vomiting, take out the tampon or cotton wool and see a health worker at once. Tell her that you have been using tampons or cotton wool.

Pieces of cloth need changing frequently and washing to prevent germs getting into the vagina and making the girl ill. Dry them in the sun.

Should girls change their behaviour during a period?

Some cultures instruct women to behave in a special way during menstruation. For example, they should eat special foods, stay in a separate house, stop cooking or not go to the mosque. Some of these rules are good because they allow the woman to rest or eat foods that make more blood. Some of these rules no longer make sense and are changing.

Activities

1 Find out what materials are available for keeping clean during periods in your village or town. How much do they cost?

2 What rules are there about menstruation in your culture? Talk to an elderly woman and find out why these rules exist and whether they are changing.

3 What are the good and bad points about these rules for women?

You can do anything you normally do during a period if you feel comfortable.

Menstruation is not an illness. However, some girls get cramps and belly pains at the start of their periods. Taking exercise can help you to avoid belly pains.

If you get bad belly pains, take some paracetamol or aspirin and lie down with something warm on your belly. Try pressing hard on the tender place between your thumb and first finger.

Some women feel tired, cross, bloated and sad in the few days before their period starts. Hormones cause these problems. You will feel better when your period starts. Try taking exercise, eating less salt, avoiding coffee, tea and coca cola and eating foods such as peanuts, fish and beans which contain protein.

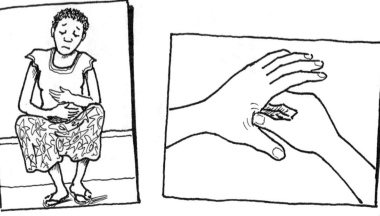

About breasts

The growth of breasts is one of the first signs of puberty in girls. The nipples grow first and then the rest of the breast. The nipples and the dark area around them, the areola, are the most sensitive to touch. Women get pleasure from having their breasts touched and sucked during breast-feeding and love-making.

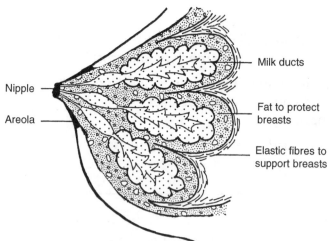

Nipple

Areola

Milk ducts

Fat to protect breasts

Elastic fibres to support breasts

The breasts grow bigger and may get a bit sore every month a few days before the period comes. Then they return to normal. Breasts get bigger during pregnancy and breast-feeding when they produce milk for the baby.

The size and shape of the breasts depends on the amount of fat stored in them. Breasts come in all shapes and sizes and they can all produce milk and give pleasure to men and women during love-making. Sometimes one breast grows faster than the other or remains bigger than the other. This is normal.

Wearing a bra may feel more comfortable and helps to support the breasts so that they do not hang down. This is most important for girls with heavy breasts.

If you notice any changes in your breasts that are different from the normal ones, visit a health worker. Changes to look out for are strange lumps of any sort, changes in shape, discharge from the nipples and pits or hollows in the skin around the breast. This could be a sign of a health problem or disease.

How do boys develop?

Boys can see their sex organs developing more easily than girls can because they are outside the body. First the **testicles** get bigger at around 12–14 years of age. The **penis** gets bigger about a year later. Penises come in different shapes and sizes. Most of the time they are small and soft but sometimes they become hard. The tube running down the middle of the penis carries urine and semen.

The smooth head of the penis is called the **glans**. This place is very sensitive to touch and gives pleasure. In uncircumcised boys, the glans is covered by the foreskin. The skin is cut off during circumcision. We discuss this further on page 22.

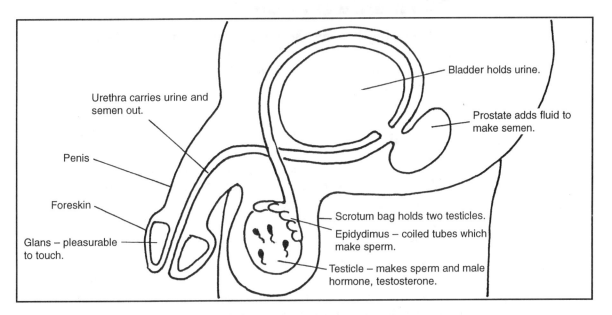

Urethra carries urine and semen out.

Bladder holds urine.

Prostate adds fluid to make semen.

Penis

Foreskin

Glans – pleasurable to touch.

Scrotum bag holds two testicles.

Epidydimus – coiled tubes which make sperm.

Testicle – makes sperm and male hormone, testosterone.

Millions of **sperm** are made all the time in little coiled tubes called the **epididymus**. If the sperm are not used, they are cleared away by the body and new ones are made. It does not do a boy any harm not to ejaculate his sperm. There are 200–500 million sperm in the semen every time a boy ejaculates. A sperm looks like a tadpole. Sperm are too small to see with the eye. They can quickly swim into the womb using their long tails to move them forward. Sometimes they can even swim into the womb if they fall outside the vagina on the vulva.

The sperm need a cooler temperature than body temperature to grow. This is why the testicles are carried outside the body in the scrotum. Sometimes the testicles stay inside the belly. The doctor can operate to put them in the scrotum. One healthy testicle is enough to make babies.

All about erections

When boys get sexually excited, the penis fills with blood, gets bigger and becomes hard and stands up. This is called an erection. This hardness enables a man to put his penis inside the vagina of the woman and have sexual intercourse.

Boys can have erections at any time when they think about sexy things or for no reason at all. This does no harm and will go away if the boy thinks about something else. If the boy is in a private place he might masturbate or play with his penis until he comes. This is normal.

What are wet dreams?

When a boy becomes sexually excited in a dream, he may have an erection and ejaculate in his sleep. This is called a wet dream. He wakes up feeling nice and finds some sticky wetness in his bed. This is natural.

Is male circumcision good or bad?

In some cultures and religions, the foreskin is cut off, leaving the glans exposed. In others, the foreskin is left. People have very strong feelings about this but either way, a man can make love, ejaculate sperm and make babies. A circumcised man may take longer to ejaculate.

If you are not circumcised, you need to pull the foreskin back to wash underneath. If you don't, germs can grow and the secretion from the glans, called smegma, will smell. If you are circumcised, your glans has no protective covering and the skin gets a little thicker.

In some cultures, circumcision is part of the initiation ceremony when boys become men. The circumcisor should sterilise the knife between the circumcision of each boy so that germs such as HIV are not passed from one boy to another. It is better to have circumcision done by a health worker.

Activities

1 Are some or all boys in your culture circumcised or not?

2 What are the good and bad things about each way?

3 How could the problems be solved?

Problem page

....

I am 15 years old and my penis is smaller than anyone I know of my age. When I urinate, friends tease me and say I will never be able to please a woman or have children.

What can I do to make my penis grow?

Boys develop at different rates and your penis may have a lot of growing to do yet. You have probably noticed that it gets bigger when it is erect.

A man with a small penis can still please a woman. Sexual intercourse is only part of pleasing a woman. Women also enjoy caressing, cuddling and kissing. A man can be such a super lover and good friend that his wife does not think about the size of his penis. A man with a small penis can still make his wife pregnant.

Learning about sexuality

Many cultures have rituals where girls and sometimes boys are taught how to behave sexually. These initiation ceremonies are dying out in some places and many parents feel shy to teach their children. Often there is no time in the school curriculum for sex education. Young people are left to pick from the old and new role models and messages around them. Ministries of Education can play a major role in improving sexual and reproductive health if they include sex education in the school curriculum.

● Activities

1 Draw a line showing your birth and your age now. This is your lifeline. Now shut your eyes and imagine that you are five years old or as far back as you can remember.

2 What messages did you get from your family, community and friends about sex? Mark the messages along your lifeline.

3 What effect do these messages have on your life? How would you change them for your children?

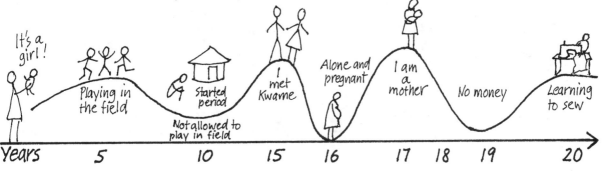

Female circumcision

In some cultures, girls have parts of their genitals cut off, often when they reach puberty. There are three types of female circumcision:

- the clitoris and its hood are cut;
- the inner labia are also removed;
- in infibulation, all the outside genitals are removed and the vulva is sewn up so that only a small hole remains for urine and menstrual blood to pass. The woman has to be cut open before she can have sex or deliver a baby.

Points of view

'I was cut when I was ten years old at my initiation ceremony. Even now, if I think of the pain, tears come to my eyes. I remember bleeding for three days until I was certain I was dying – all my blood had drained away. I heard my mother calling for the spirits to save me. Well, I lived to marry when I was 20 years old. My husband was a good man, but we could not enjoy our sex life because it caused me such pain. I have never had the blessing of sexual happiness through my whole marriage.

I have lost my 'pleasure button' as those fortunate enough to have a clitoris call it. I wish there were a shop where I could buy one. Eventually I became pregnant. The delivery nearly killed me. I had to be cut again and re-sewn. I shall never have another child. Now my daughter is nine years old, I shall never allow her to be cut. I keep her with me in town. I never visit my family in the village with her in case she is snatched away and cut. If I travel my sister cares for her.'

'I think that we should continue with our traditions. The circumcision helps girls to bear pain and gives them a group of 'sisters' for life. The circumcision stops girls wanting sex so they find it easy to keep their virginity and be faithful. It is easier for them to marry well and they and their families feel proud. They are respected and loved by their husbands. An uncircumcised girl will never find a husband.'

'My first wife was circumcised and I don't believe that she ever enjoyed sex. Sadly she died in childbirth and I later married a woman from an ethnic group who do not circumcise. I love my wife and I enjoy our sexual relations because we can both have pleasure. I don't worry about her being unfaithful because she is satisfied with the love we have together. We do not intend to have our daughter cut. If a man does not want to marry her because of that, he does not love her or believe in himself.'

'I used to be a circumcisor. But I always feared cutting too deep and every year one or two mother's daughters would not return home. I shut my ears to their pain because I convinced myself that it was good. After all it was done to me. Now I think it's right to call it mutilation. I was robbed of my birthright – to have pleasure in sex. Now I still teach the girls in the initiation ceremony. I teach them the best of our traditions but also new ideas about health and love. I don't do any cutting but the girls learn the importance of treating sex with respect and caution. They behave well and receive the respect they used to get from cutting. And I still have my power and rewards.'

'I was circumcised when I was a little girl. When I went to secondary school I met girls who had not been circumcised and I learnt that I had lost a great source of pleasure for women. My parents wanted me to marry a certain man but before I did, I fell in love with a man at my training college. We loved each other so much that he could touch me in any place, on my ears, my feet, my waist and I would get so excited. We married and to this day, the feelings I get when he makes love to me are so strong and wonderful that I have orgasms any time. I have also found a place in my vagina that feels very good when it is stroked and when I clench my vaginal muscles when we move together, I climax easily. So I would like to tell my sisters who have been circumcised – don't despair. Talk to your man about how to stroke you all over and please you until you are aroused. Practise squeezing your vaginal muscles secretly until they are strong and feel inside for your sensitive place. If sex is painful, wait until you are wet before he enters you or use some slippery substance like baby oil. If the hole is too small, see whether a health worker could make it larger for you.'

Health problems caused by female circumcision

These problems may happen straight after circumcision or in the first week.

Heavy bleeding is very dangerous. The girl can lose a lot of blood and go into shock and die. If she is very thirsty, cold and pale with a weak and fast pulse, fast breathing and fainting, GET HELP IMMEDIATELY.

Press a clean small cloth firmly on the bleeding spot. Help her to drink a lot and carry her lying down to medical help.

Infection: If the cutting tool is not cleaned with bleach before and after each use, germs can cause wound infection, tetanus, hepatitis or HIV/AIDS. If a girl shows signs of shock, fever, confusion or tight jaw, stiff neck and body muscles, difficulty swallowing and convulsions, TAKE HER TO MEDICAL HELP AT ONCE.

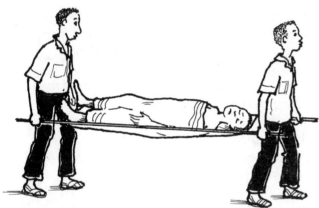

Urine problems: Circumcision causes pain on urinating so some girls try to hold their urine back. This can cause infection and damage the urine tubes, bladder and kidneys. Girls can lessen the pain by drinking lots of water, running clean water over the genitals while passing urine and applying a damp cloth soaked in warm water to the genitals. If a girl has not passed urine for more than a day or a night, and her lower belly feels tight and full over the bladder, TAKE HER TO MEDICAL HELP AT ONCE.

Problems with monthly bleeding: If the vaginal hole left after circumcision is too small, the monthly blood flow can be blocked. This can cause painful periods, long periods or no monthly bleeding. Trapped blood can cause serious pelvic infection, damage to the womb and tubes and infertility.

A towel soaked in hot water held on the lower belly or light exercise can help to relieve pain. If the problem is very bad, seek medical help to make the hole larger.

Problems with sexual relations and sexual health: Many women who have been circumcised, especially if they are sewn up, find sex difficult. Sex is especially painful and dangerous if a woman is circumcised on the same day as marriage or if she is cut to make the hole bigger just before marriage. The wound may take longer to heal and she is at more risk of HIV or STDs. If this happens in your area, help men to understand that the opening should be gently and safely made larger by a health worker a long time before first intercourse. The wound must be completely healed before having sex.

Problems with childbirth: Scars from circumcision can make it very difficult for the baby to be born and can cause bad tearing and bleeding during delivery. It is best for girls to plan for delivery in advance so that the midwife can tell them of any problems and enlarge the hole long before the birth if necessary.

Leaking stool and urine: Some couples do anal sex if the vaginal hole is too small. This can cause leaking of stool from the anus. Blocked childbirth can cause holes in the bladder and rectum leading to leaking urine and faeces. This often results in a girl being rejected by her partner and family.

Mental health problems: A girl who has been circumcised may feel sad, anxious or fearful. She may feel that she can trust no-one and that she has no control over her life. Pain and suffering can cause depression and low self-esteem. Sexual problems may cause marital stress and breakdown.

Counselling and forming a support group for girls who have been circumcised can help girls to recover emotionally from their experiences. The secrecy of circumcision stops girls from sharing their suffering with others, weeping together and healing. It is good to end the secrecy for this reason and so that people can decide together whether it is a good custom or they want to change it.

• Activities

1 Draw a flow chart to show all the good points and all the bad points about female circumcision.

2 Discuss the question: Are the benefits of being circumcised worth the health problems? Culture is always changing in response to new ideas and needs. Can this practice also be changed?

3 Many people believe that female circumcision violates girls' human rights to bodily integrity, safety and health and their right to privacy and choice because it is done to children who are not old enough to agree to the practice. What do you think?

4 What can you do to change the practice in your community and support those who are suffering?

3 Feeling good and doing well

In this chapter, we look at how we feel about ourselves and how we can communicate well with our families, friends and partners. If we think that we are valuable people, we believe that we deserve care and respect. We have the confidence to talk clearly about our thoughts and feelings, our rights and dreams. We can learn to make good decisions so that we achieve our goals and keep ourselves safe. We can take responsibility for our actions and expect others to do the same.

What is self-esteem?

Self-esteem is the way that we feel about ourselves. We create this picture of ourselves in a number of ways:

- from the feedback that we receive from other people – they act as a mirror, giving us a picture of who we are;
- from the expectations of our society – if we are different from what they expect, this can lower our self-esteem;
- from our own experiences – every time we achieve something, our self-esteem rises;
- from our imagination of the future.

Activities

1 Draw a picture of yourself to show the things that make you proud and the things that you would like to change.

2 For each point, think about why you feel this way.

Women often have lower self-esteem than men because they are brought up to believe that they are less valuable.

How can we develop high self-esteem and confidence in ourselves?

We can change the way we see ourselves and help each other to develop more confidence in the following ways.

- Listen to each other and value the words we each say.

- Tell each other when we have done well, the things we like about each other, our strengths.

- Know that each of us is special and unique.

- Each of us experiences life in our own way. Let's learn how it is to be in each other's shoes and accept each other.

- We give ourselves messages about what we are feeling, thinking and doing all the time. Sometimes we say good things about ourselves and sometimes bad. Sometimes our conscience tells us we have done wrong and should make things better. Sometimes we are too hard on ourselves.

- Our family and friends can help us to feel good about ourselves. Sometimes they forget to praise us, they only criticise us. This lowers our self-esteem. We can encourage people to praise us by praising them. We can criticise people in a helpful way that does not make them feel bad and take care that teasing does not hurt.

- Being good at something helps us to gain confidence, whether it's basket weaving or maths. Practise your skill until you are good at it. Then when you are feeling bad, say to yourself 'Yes, but I'm very good at ... .'

- We all make mistakes – that's how we learn. We do not need to feel bad every time we make a mistake. Let's just admit that we made a mistake and learn from it.

- Let's believe that we can achieve things. One small step can lead to another until we have travelled a long way.

I did really badly at maths.

But I'm brilliant at drama!

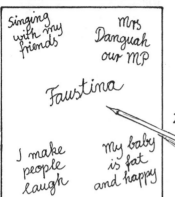

1 Write your name in the middle of a piece of paper. In the left top corner write or draw 'My favourite activity'; in the right top corner, 'The woman or man I admire'; the bottom left corner 'The best thing about me is …'; and the bottom right corner 'My greatest achievement'. Pin the paper on your chest and move around the room looking at each other's papers and talking about what you see there.

2 Finish the sentence: 'I am valuable and important because …'

Someone who took one small step and travelled a long way

Respect

We respect those we admire for their good qualities. We treat them politely and listen to their ideas. If we have high self-esteem, we respect ourselves and accept our good qualities. We may treat people with respect because they have high status. For example, women may show respect to men by kneeling in front of them. However, we also have to earn respect by behaving well. A drunken father loses the respect of his family. In many societies, respect for elders, men and people in authority, based only on their status, has weakened. People have to deserve respect through their good qualities and behaviour.

● Activity   Discuss the two pictures below.

What is the effect of the teacher's behaviour on: a) the pupils' respect for him and each other and b) their behaviour?

Talking to each other

The way that we communicate with each other is important for our relationships. We use words to express our thoughts and feelings. Our faces, hand movements and the way we hold our bodies send messages about our feelings and self-esteem.

One third of our communication is understood through words and two thirds through our body language. If we say we are angry but smile, no one will believe us.

Men and women and young and older people sometimes find it difficult to communicate well. They may give words different meanings or feel put down by what the other says.

We can learn to express our thoughts and feelings clearly to show friendship, love and a desire to understand each other.

● **Activity**

In a still picture from a drama scene, people pose very carefully, thinking about their facial expression, body language and how they are placed in relation to each other. They do not say anything. In pairs, pose to make a picture to show something about the relationship between two people. It could be a boy and girl, an adult and child or two friends.

Show your pictures and ask people what they can see. What does the body language of the two people tell us about their relationship? How does this apply to our lives?

Some important communication skills

- Listen carefully to what people say, look at their body language as well as the words and check that you have understood their ideas and feelings.

- Ask questions that encourage people to talk and show interest in their feelings and what is happening in their lives.

  - Put yourself in the other person's shoes. Think how it would feel to be them.

Mum, you look sad. What's the matter?

Different ways of behaving

We learn how to behave from an early age, depending on our culture and gender. In many societies, girls are taught to behave in a submissive way to men. They are taught to lower their eyes, to sit at a lower level than the men, to crouch down and to speak softly. They are expected to satisfy the needs of their husband, in-laws and children and to keep quiet about their own needs. Girls who do not learn to behave in a womanly way are punished until they do.

Women are taught to adopt **passive** behaviour. This means that they:

- allow boys or men to make all the decisions;
- do not give their opinion;
- do not start something new;
- keep their feelings hidden;
- try to keep the peace at all costs.

Boys and men are often allowed to behave in a more **aggressive** way. They can show anger openly through shouting, hitting or threatening someone.

Assertive behaviour is when someone says what they feel, think and would like clearly and honestly in a way that is good for themselves and the other person. Assertive behaviour can increase your confidence and control over your life. People respect you more and relationships improve.

How to be assertive

- Tell people your thoughts and feelings clearly and honestly. Say 'I' feel or think or would like. Do not apologise for saying what you think or put yourself down.

- Hold your head up, stand and sit straight in a relaxed way, make eye contact and match your facial expression to what you are saying.

- Speak so that people can hear you clearly.

Father, I would feel so happy if you could use some of the money from the cocoa harvest to pay for my school fee.

- Accept other people's right to say 'No' and learn how to say 'No' yourself.

- Accept compliments and feel good about yourself. Accept true criticisms and learn from them.

- If you make a mistake, say sorry. If someone says sorry to you, forgive him or her.

- Be principled and live by that. Respect yourself.

- Learn how to say that you feel angry in a way that does not harm other people.

- Do not be afraid of disagreeing with people. If everyone is able to say what they think clearly and co-operate to find solutions, everyone can 'win' in the end.

We all want to be accepted in a group and one way of achieving this is to agree with its members and do what everyone else does. Pressure from our peers to behave like them can be very strong and difficult to resist. However, if you stand up for yourself and what you believe, people often respect you more and like you better.

Points of view

Tefinas: 'One day my neighbour proposed love to me. I wanted to treat him with respect so I said politely 'Thank you Sir, but I am a schoolgirl and I have to go home now to do my studies'. Still he persisted more strongly so I looked him in the eye and said 'When you say such things I feel bad because I am a young girl and you are old enough to be my father. I do not want such friendship with you and I would like you to go away and not bother me again'. He looked very embarrassed and left me.'

Omuge: 'I used to say to girls 'I want you now, this minute, like it or not!' Now I say 'I would feel very happy if we could enjoy ourselves together. What do you say?' The girl then also makes the decision and feels good. If she says 'no', I have to respect that.'

Sylvia: 'My aunt said it was time I got married and she wanted me to meet a young man from the village. I managed to say to her 'My aunt, I feel that I am too young to marry now, I should like to wait until I have finished my studies and I am more mature to make a good wife and mother'. After some more talking, she agreed with me and she hasn't talked of marriage again. I was surprised how good it felt to say what I wanted and be heard.'

1 In pairs, role-play a problem situation that happened to you recently. For example, your friends are doing something that makes you unhappy; you made a mistake; you are not getting on well with your mother. Perform the role play and invite members of the audience to replay it so that things go better.

2 Discuss the following question:

If girls and women behave more assertively, will they become more equal and powerful? What barriers might make it difficult for this to happen? What else would need to change at the same time?

Making decisions

Sometimes we make our decisions on the basis of our feelings. If something feels right we do it without thinking too much about it. This can work well and women are good at making decisions in this way. However, sometimes our feelings are not a good guide to decision-making. For example, if we feel very sexy, we may not think about the possible bad results of having sexual intercourse.

Sometimes it is better to make a decision by looking at the good and bad things about each option and deciding which one is best for us. It is good to make decisions in this way because we see that we have some choices but not others. Girls often have fewer choices than boys and poor people have fewer choices than rich. If we use our imagination together, we might find some new choices that we had not thought of before. Once we see how our own fears or expectations, people around us or our environment block our choices, we might want to work towards changing things.

Some decisions are very important in our lives. We should stop to think before we act and recognise that these are important decisions. Decisions about sexual relationships are very important.

Decisions are based on what we believe in and our thoughts.

A decision tree

Questions to ask when making a decision:

- Where am I now?
- What are my goals? Where do I want to be?
- What are my choices for getting there?
- What are the advantages and disadvantages of each choice?
- What resources do I need for each choice?
- Who would support me if I made this choice? Who do I need to involve in the decision?
- What would help and hinder me in this choice?
- What might the good and bad results of that choice be?
- What steps do I need to take action on my decision?

Let's look at the story of Mary who is trying to make a decision about what to do next year when she finishes primary school.

● Activity

Help Mary to make her decision by role-playing the story and talking over the questions with her. Use diagrams to make the pros and cons of the different choices easier to see.

I have just finished primary school. I have got good enough grades to go to secondary school. A man in the village has asked my parents if he can marry me. My aunty who lives in the city has suggested that I go to work as an apprentice in her sewing business.

What shall I do?

Taking risks

We all take risks in our lives. When we get into a bus or have a baby we risk death or illness. If we fall in love, we risk getting hurt if they leave us. If we take a risk and it works out well, people admire us. If we take a risk and it works out badly, they blame us. We can learn to think before taking a risk, try to reduce risks as much as possible and take risks that are likely to work out well.

1 Think of a time when you took a risk.

- Why did you take the risk?
- Did it turn out well or badly?
- Could you have done anything to make the risk smaller?
- What other choices did you have?
- Do you think you take a lot of risks or a few?
- What do you think about friends who take risks? .

2 Role-play a situation where your friend is about to take a risk and you are worried that it will turn out badly. What will you do?

When we make decisions and take risks, we have some responsibility for the results of our actions. We now look at how responsible we are and how we can become more responsible.

Being responsible

 ### Quiz: How responsible are you?

....

1 You get a sexually transmitted disease. Do you:

   a) tell your lover that it was your fault and offer to pay for his or her treatment; (3)

   b) tell all your friends in town to avoid your lover but don't tell him or her; (1)

   c) talk it over with your lover to understand how the problem came about and suggest that he or she goes for treatment? (2)

2 You have no condoms but you and your friend are feeling hot. Do you:

   a) have sex anyway; (1)

   b) walk miles in the dark to find some condoms; (3)

   c) have a great time talking and kissing? (2)

3 You borrow a book from a friend and it gets soaked in the rain. Do you:

   a) dry it out and apologise to her; (2)

   b) say that you left it for her in the classroom and someone must have taken it; (1)

   c) borrow money to buy her a new book and a present? (3)

4 Your friend has gone off with a truck driver because she is angry with her parents. Do you:

    a) say that if she gets in trouble, it serves her right;   (1)

    b) get together with another friend and follow the truck;   (3)

    c) tell your friend's favourite aunt where she has gone?   (2)

5 Your friend gets very drunk and you can see that he or she is behaving dangerously. Do you:

    a) laugh with the others and hope that it will be all right;   (1)

    b) take your friend home and next day talk with them about their behaviour;   (2)

    c) go with your friend everywhere to make sure that they are safe?   (3)

6 You see a friend of yours beating another friend. Do you:

    a) pretend that you haven't seen them and walk away;   (1)

    b) go up and start beating your aggressive friend;   (3)

    c) go up and try to hold him off and calm him down?   (2)

··

> Add up your points to see how responsible you are.

15–18   You take on responsibility easily but sometimes you take responsibility for problems which are not of your making. This can get you into trouble or make the people around you avoid taking responsibility.

10–14   You are a responsible person. You behave in ways that prevent harming others. You say that you have made a mistake and try to repair the damage that you have done. You take responsibility for the welfare of others but also give them joint responsibility as equals.

6–9   You do not agree that you have any responsibility when things go wrong. You blame others and do not try to prevent problems or make things better when they go wrong.

We tend to say 'it's not my fault' when things go wrong and blame others. We act without thinking of the consequences; we take risks that affect other people without telling them. Alcohol and drugs make us forget our responsibilities. Our culture may tell us that we are not responsible for an area of life, although our actions affect that area. Women are often given responsibility for stopping before sexual intercourse, preventing pregnancy and sexually transmitted diseases, childcare and keeping the peace. This can make men feel that they do not have to be responsible for these things.

It is better if women and men share responsibility for their behaviour and what happens in relationships. We can all:

- **agree** and **tell** each other when we are responsible for an action or have done something wrong;

- **accept** our part of the responsibility, and tell other parties assertively what is their share of the responsibility;

- **act** to prevent problems or to repair the damage we have done;

4 Friendship, love, sex and marriage

We have relationships with many different people in our lives. We begin with our family and then make friends outside our homes. Later we interact with many other adults like teachers and nurses. When we reach puberty, we start to get interested in people in a sexual way. Our bodies tingle, our hearts beat faster, we feel happy to be near them and want to get closer.

How well we get on with people is important for our whole lives. If our relationships with our family and friends are good, and later our husbands/wives and children, we feel safe and secure and have stronger relationships with other people.

• Activity

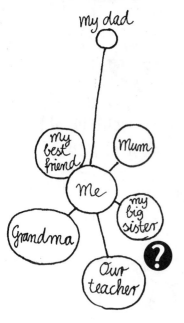

Make a diagram with you in the middle to show the important people in your life. Make big circles for important people and put them closer to you.

Why are these people important to you? What good things have they given you and what do you give them in return?

Friendship is very important to all of us. Good friends can last for a lifetime and support us even when life gets tough. We can all learn how to be a better friend throughout our lives.

? Quiz: How responsible are you?

1 Imagine that one of your favourite cousins died. Would you:
  a) keep your sorrow to yourself and try to act as if nothing has happened; (1)
  b) tell your close friends about your cousin and weep; (2)
  c) tell your friends to mind their own business when they ask what is wrong? (3)

2 Your friend is upset because her/his boyfriend/girlfriend has left her. Do you:

  a) tell her some jokes to take her/his mind off her problem;   (1)

  b) tell her/him that the same thing happened to you and launch into the whole story;   (3)

  c) encourage her/him to tell you about it and listen carefully?   (2)

3 Your friend turns up in a beautiful dress. Do you:

  a) tell her how nice she looks;   (2)

  b) ask her which boyfriend paid for it;   (3)

  c) say nothing to her but feel envious?   (1)

4 Your friend gets very drunk one night and flirts with your girlfriend/boyfriend. Do you:

  a) say nothing and decide to end the friendship;   (1)

  b) punch him/her on the nose;   (3)

  c) tell both of them your feelings the next day?   (2)

5 You failed your science exam and your friend was top of the class. Do you:

  a) tell everyone your friend is a boring know-it-all;   (3)

  b) congratulate your friend and ask if he/she can help you with science;   (2)

  c) say nothing, keep away from your friend and feel bad?   (1)

6 Your friend thinks that female genital mutilation is a good tradition. You think it should be stopped. Do you:

  a) pretend that you think it is good too;   (1)

  b) tell your friend about your ideas about FGM and the reasons why you want it stopped;   (2)

  c) shout at your friend that she/he is still living in primitive times and you don't need a dinosaur as a friend?   (3)

7 Your friend owes someone money and he is demanding payment. Do you:

  a) help him/her find ways to repay the money;   (2)

  b) say that you'll help him/her if he/she'll do you a favour;   (3)

  c) avoid him/her until she has sorted it out?   (1)

Add up your points and see what kind of friend you are.

7–11   You keep your feelings hidden and try to avoid conflict. You do not want to hear about your friends' feelings or problems either. You find it difficult to talk openly about personal matters. Try to express your thoughts and feelings more with your friends.

12–15   You are a good friend. You share your happy and sad feelings with your friends and listen to them when they have problems and look for practical ways to solve them. You are able to praise your friends and forgive them. You can challenge them when you disagree with them, without putting them down.

16–21   You are aggressive to your friends and more interested in yourself than them. Try to listen more and put yourself in their shoes.

What is love?

All languages have words for love. Some have different words for friendship love and sexual love. Some languages have only one word for love, perhaps expressing the idea that friendship and sex should go hand in hand.

Letter page

....

Dear Uncle Olu

My friend Rosie and I have been going around together since primary school. I really love her. We can talk about anything, relax together and be ourselves. We are interested in each other's problems and we laugh and cry together. We enjoy challenging each other at schoolwork and at weekends we go to a singing group. Now I have met this girl called Serena and I think I have fallen in love with her. I think about her all the time. I want to be with her, hear her voice, touch her. And yet sometimes I can't think of one word to say. She likes the cinema and is working. I often do not have time to see Rosie now and I know that she feels sad, but I have to be around in case Serena comes by. Is it possible to love two people? Is there more than one kind of love and if so which one is best?   Kwame

• Activities

1 What would you say to Kwame?

2 What words do you have in your language for love?

3 How do we know that we love someone or that they love us?

4 How do we behave towards someone we love and how do we expect a person who loves us to behave?

Having sexual feelings

As boys and girls reach puberty, they often start to have sexual feelings. They may feel tingling or warm feelings when they think about or touch a particular person. These feelings can run around the body like an electric current and arouse strong feelings in the genital area and breasts. Boys may have erections and girls feel wet. These feelings are natural and good, they mean that you are growing up. However, what you do with these feelings is important. Just because you feel excited by someone does not mean that you have to do anything about it. You can make a choice about whether to show your sexual feelings and in what way.

- You might decide to enjoy the feelings without doing anything about them at all. This will not make you sick or mad.
- You might spend more time with the person, getting to know them better, talking, studying or working together.
- You might stroke and play with your sexual parts (genitals) and breasts privately. This is called masturbation.
- You might kiss, caress and cuddle the person.
- You might decide to have sexual intercourse with them.

• Activity Divide into groups. Each group looks at the advantages and disadvantages of one of the options for young people of their age and sex, listed above. Share ideas with the other groups.

Falling in love

Falling in love is a very powerful feeling. We find one person who is very special to us, who we want to be with, listen to, touch and get close to with our minds, hearts and bodies. We can be open with our friend, talk about anything without fear and show our feelings. We trust each other and feel that this person is on our side and will love us whatever happens.

What is sexual health?

Sexual health is when we feel good in relation to that area of our lives to do with sex. We feel good in our bodies, minds, spirit, feelings and in our society.

Sexual health includes:

- making decisions about our own bodies and how and when we will express our sexuality without anyone forcing or pressuring us; being able to say 'no' to sex until we are mature, in a loving relationship and happy to say 'yes';

- if we do have sex, protecting ourselves from unwanted pregnancy and diseases that are passed during sex, called Sexually Transmitted Diseases;

- enjoying pleasure from sex and being sexy without harming others;

- enjoying our sexuality free from shame, guilt and fear;

- visiting the health centre if we have a problem.

Different kinds of sexual relationships

Sexual relationships can give us great joy and great pain.

People have many different kinds of sexual relationship. Society approves of some of them more than others. If we are in an approved relationship we can talk about it and go around together openly. We have to keep relationships that are not approved of secret.

All societies and religions approve of sex within marriage when it leads to children. Few people approve of sex between people of the same sex. Sex with close relatives and children is against the law in most societies.

People have sex for many different reasons from love to money or force.

People may have one sexual relationship in their lives or many; they may have relationships one after the other or at the same time.

Many people have times in their lives when they are not in a sexual relationship. This is fine.

1 Make a 'But why' tree to show all the reasons why young people might have sex. Start by putting a picture or symbol in the middle to depict two people having sex. Now think of all the reasons why someone might have sex and write or draw them on pieces of paper. Put the reasons around the middle picture in order with the immediate reason first and the underlying causes of that reason next and so on. For each reason, ask 'But why' to find out the underlying cause. Stop when you run out of ideas.

2 Which of these reasons gives the person a free choice to say 'yes' or 'no' to sex?

Making your own decisions about sex

Many sexual health problems arise because women (and sometimes men) do not have control over their sexual lives. In many cultures, women are the property of fathers, brothers, husbands or the extended family. Fathers can exchange their young daughters with older husbands or traders for cows or money. Husbands are entitled to have sex with their wives whenever they feel like it, regardless of the wife's feelings or health. Women may be given nicknames or teased for refusing sex. In the world of work, women are often forced to have sex to get or keep a job.

Girls are often influenced by their society to believe that their bodies are shameful, that nice girls do not know about, talk about or enjoy sex.

The low status of women means that many women have less education and lower paying jobs and therefore are poorer. With few ways to earn money, girls and women are pushed into selling sex for goods, favours or money.

Shall I have sexual intercourse or not?

If you can decide freely whether to have sex or not, think very carefully before you act. This is one of the most important decisions in your life because the consequences can be good or very bad.

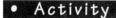

Ask for two volunteers to role-play a boy and a girl who are thinking about whether to have sex or not. Either boys or girls could play the parts. Help them to get into their characters by asking them questions about themselves, their relationship and the present situation.

Perform the role play up to the point when each person is going to make a decision on whether to have sex or not. Then 'hot seat' them. Ask them to stay in role while the audience ask each of them the questions below in any order they wish.

- What are your reasons for having sex?
- Why are you thinking of having sex with *this* person?
- Do you desire him or her? How do you know this?
- Will you be able to have sex in a private place and take enough time to enjoy it?
- Are you sober? If not, would you want to have sex with this person if you were sober?
- Do you want to have a child with this person? Does he or she want to have a child with you?
- Will you be able to obtain and use a contraceptive (such as condoms or pills) successfully?
- Contraceptives can fail. If this happens, could you have a safe abortion? How would your life change if you have to bring up a child? Will your partner share the responsibility?
- Could either of you have a Sexually Transmitted Disease or HIV infection? Will you be able to use condoms?
- Have you talked about having sex with this person?

When they have answered all the questions, ask them to talk together and decide whether to have sex or not.

Discuss their decision in the group. What are the good and bad points about it?

Abstinence

Abstinence means that a person does not have sexual intercourse.

What are the advantages of abstinence?

- Abstinence is the only 100 per cent safe way of protecting yourself from pregnancy, STDs and HIV. If you abstain, you will not have any anxieties about these problems.
- If you value sex as something very special only to be done with your spouse, you will feel happy with yourself for keeping to your values.
- If your friends and parents value sex as something for marriage, you will be socially accepted and have a good reputation.
- You will be able to enjoy yourself with friends without tying yourself up in a sexual relationship. You can get to know many people and this will help you to choose a good partner when you are ready.
- You will not risk being emotionally hurt or used.
- You may have more emotional energy for education and skills training.

Talking about abstinence

- Be clear that you do not want to have sex.
- Practise saying that you don't want to have sex with a friend.
- Explain clearly your reasons for not wanting to have sex yet.
- Discuss what would happen if you got pregnant or caught an STD or HIV.
- Say that you want to protect your fertility and life until you are ready to have a baby.
- Say that you can love someone without having sex with them.
- Say that you want to enjoy spending time together, having fun and building trust before you begin to have sex.
- Find a safe place to talk, where you won't be tempted to get romantic. Say I want to talk to you now, before we go too far.
- Discuss situations that will make it difficult for you to abstain. How will you avoid these situations?
- Go out with other friends. Avoid being alone together.
- Agree to stay away from alcohol and drugs because these make it harder to abstain.

- If you feel very sexy, try doing something physical like sports, running, gardening or dancing. Or get together with some friends.
- Say that you think sex before you are living together or married is wrong. Explain how you would feel if you went against your beliefs.
- Talk about your goals and where you want to be in three years time. Say that having a baby or getting sick would upset these goals.
- Talk about what your parents hope for you and how they would feel if you got pregnant or caught HIV.

• Activities

1 In groups of three, role-play talking about abstinence with a boy or girlfriend. Talk about what helps you and what makes it difficult. Role-play the lines that boys or girls use to persuade friends to have sex and find good ways to answer them. Find ways to resist pressures to have sex but still keep wanted friendships.

2 Role-play a group of friends teasing you because you are not having sex. They say you are old-fashioned, immature and think you are holier than them. What will you say to them?

Points of view

'I am a Catholic girl and I have decided to wait until I marry to have sex. I don't find it difficult now to say 'no' because I have lots of friends and I enjoy my studies. Maybe it will be harder if I fall in love, but I am very determined to follow my faith.'

'I fell in love with Lani when I was 17 years old. I wanted to just be friends with her until we knew each other really well and I was sure that we were properly together. We enjoyed ourselves for almost a year, just being together, talking and romancing. But it got more and more difficult to stop at the kissing, we wanted so much to be as close as a man and woman can be. I didn't have mohey to pay dowry, so she moved in with me. We are using condoms until we are ready to have a child and we are very happy together.'

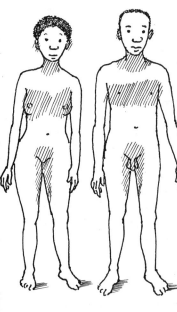

Sex and pleasure

Men and women have a right to sexual pleasure. The best sex is where there is enjoyment for both partners.

Do you think that sexual pleasure is important for both men and women?

Some women find out what pleases them and have an orgasm for the first time when they masturbate. This helps them to tell their partner what they like.

Women and men have parts of their bodies that respond to touch with sexual excitement. The clitoris, a special place at the front of the vagina called the 'G' spot and the breasts are very sensitive to touch in women. However, almost any spot can become sensitive if it is associated with love and sexuality.

When women become sexually excited, the vagina becomes wet and the clitoris, nipples and inner and outer genital lips (labia) swell and become more sensitive. The heart beats faster and the breathing rate increases. Women tend to get sexually excited more slowly than men and they need time to be touched and kissed before reaching the same point of arousal as a man.

As sexual excitement increases, the woman may have an orgasm. This is the peak of sexual excitement and gives the woman great pleasure as the vagina and pelvic muscles have waves of contractions.

I love it when you scratch my back.

When men become excited, the penis becomes erect and the heart and breathing rates increase. Men generally get aroused more quickly than women and reach orgasm earlier. When men have an orgasm, they usually ejaculate and semen containing sperm shoots out of the penis.

Men and women can enjoy sex more if they care about each other's pleasure and talk about or show what pleases them.

Mmm – and I love it when you nibble my ear.

49

Same sex friends and lovers

As we grow up, we often make close friends with people of the same sex. We feel love and affection for them and we may express our affection by hugging, kissing and stroking.

When we get older, most people become more interested sexually in people of the opposite sex.

Some people realise that they are attracted to people of the same sex. In some countries, these people call themselves 'gay' to show that they are happy to be the way they are. Loving a person of the same sex is called 'homosexuality' and of the opposite sex 'heterosexuality'.

A woman who is attracted to women is called a lesbian. A man who is attracted to the same sex is called a homosexual, a gay man or a man who has sex with men.

People may express their sexuality with a person of the same sex at certain times of their lives without seeing themselves as 'gay'. For example, girls and boys in boarding schools may have close friendships and play with each other sexually, but still see themselves as people who will get married later.

Gay people can kiss, caress and cuddle in the same ways as men and women. Some men have anal sex (the man puts his penis in the other man's anus). They can protect themselves from infection by using condoms.

In many countries, homosexuality is strongly disapproved of, or illegal. This forces people who have these feelings to hide them. Society's disapproval makes it difficult for gay people to stay with a regular partner in a long-term relationship and this puts them at risk of HIV.

It is very difficult to be different from all your friends and to be considered an outcast even by your own family.

Points of view

'I am Daniel. I suffered as I was growing up because I realised that I was different from my friends but I never dared to say so. I lived with this secret for a long time. I think that people have a right to be true to their own feelings and love the person whom they feel love for. Nobody asks to be born lesbian or gay because you are treated badly by society. I want to set up an organisation that helps gay people and lesbians to be open about being gay, to feel good about themselves and to fight against unfair treatment.'

'I'm Mary. I think homosexuality is disgusting and should be treated as an illness. God made men and women to have sex so that they can have children. If there are no children, it is wrong.'

what do you think?

Activities

1 In groups of boys only and girls only, draw around a person's body either on the wall or floor with chalk or on a large piece of paper. Invite people to mark on the outline places on the body where they feel pleasure when they are touched by someone they love. How could you tell your boy or girlfriend where you like to be touched?

Now draw places where you do not like to be touched by a person who you do not love sexually. How could you stop someone doing this to you?

2 In groups of boys only and girls only, make four squares on the board or a piece of paper. In each square put 'Things that turn girls on', 'Things that turn girls off', 'Things that turn boys on', 'Things that turn boys off' (to turn on means to sexually arouse).

When you have filled in all the squares, get all the groups together and share your ideas.

● How well did boys know what pleases girls?

● How well did girls know what pleases boys?

● How could this knowledge help people to have happy relationships?

● Could this knowledge be used to seduce somebody so that they have sex when they did not intend or want to?

Saying what you want in sex

Our bodies are our own. We all have the right to choose whether, when and how to have sex as long as the other person agrees. It is important to learn to say clearly what we feel and want in sexual situations. It is a human right to have sex and also to refuse sex if we do not want it.

In new relationships, a 'good' girl is expected to say 'no' to a proposal for love, even if she intends to say 'yes'. She is expected to be polite and not offend the boy even if she is really saying 'no'.

Boys may think that when a girl says 'no' she is playing hard to get. Boys may find it hard to say 'no' to a woman who proposes love to them.

A girl or boy may want to say 'no, not now'. This can lead to quarrels.

We may not always want to say 'no' to sex! We want to say 'yes' but let's do it in a way that ensures we are both happy and healthy.

• Activities

1 In groups of girls only and boys only, pairs practise saying what they want in a sexual encounter. They then show their role plays to each other and discuss what worked well and why?

2 Role-play a situationss where one person is proposing love and the other person wants to agree but is at first saying 'no'. How do you know whether the person means 'no' or not?

3 Role-play situation where you want to say 'no, not now' in a way that does not hurt or offend the other person, but helps them to listen to and understand your needs.

4 Role-play situations where you are really saying 'no'. Invite everyone to show how they would say 'no' so the person knows they mean it. In pairs, practise saying 'no' to show you mean it.

5 Now role-play a situation where the person refused to take any notice of the 'no' and continued to demand sex more aggressively. Invite people to role-play how they would handle this. Let everyone practise saying 'no' in this situation.

   • How does it feel when your partner refuses to listen to your 'no'?

Come on, you know you want to....

- Why do some people force others to have sex even though they do not want it? How does this affect sexual relationships?

6 Choose three of your role plays to present to the opposite sex group. Try to reach agreement that when a person says 'no' in a certain way they mean it and their wish should be respected.

7 Role-play situations where you say 'yes' but tell your partner what you want in some way, for example, more kissing and touching or using a condom.

Listen to me – I said 'No', I do not want to. I would feel happy to talk and cuddle, but if this is not OK for you I'm going home.

What can you do if there is no pleasure?

Sex can give us all great pleasure but sometimes we do not enjoy it. Here are the views of some people who did not enjoy sex.

Points of view

'I stopped enjoying sex after my husband beat me. I hated and feared him and vowed that I would never respond to him again.'

'My boyfriend and I can only grab sex quickly in the bushes. I am afraid someone will see us and it hurts because I am dry.'

'I am too afraid of getting pregnant to enjoy sex. He always says he will withdraw, so I wait nervously for him to pull out.'

'Women are not supposed to enjoy sex, it is shameful.'

'My boyfriend does 'cock sex', straight in and out, no romancing   how can I have an orgasm? It's too quick. My grandmother said men used to know how to play with their beads to turn them on, but these young men have forgotten. I wish I could talk to him about what I like.'

What would you say to each of these people and their partners?

Painful sex

If sex is painful, there is something wrong.

Sex may be painful because of a lack of wetness from sexual excitement. This happens if sex is too rushed or forced or if the woman has dried out her vagina. Dry sex is risky because it can damage the wall of the vagina making it easier for HIV or germs to go through. Men should always take time to arouse the woman before sex. Do not try to dry the vagina. The wetness is normal and protects women.

Infections can cause painful sex and lead to serious health problems. Go to the health centre at once if you think you have an infection.

Sex may be painful if a young girl has sex with an older man with a big penis.

Female circumcision may make the entrance to the vagina too small so that sex can tear the vagina. Take a lot of time to gently stretch the entrance or see a health worker.

If a girl is afraid of sex, she may tighten the muscles around the vagina causing sex to be painful.

In the next section, we look more closely at marriage because most men and women in Africa get married at least once in their lives. Marriage is a big step that can improve a person's life or make it worse.

Marriage

There are different types of marriages in African cultures. A man may marry only one wife or two or more. In some communities, girls marry at a young age, even before puberty. Sometimes young girls marry older men. However, young people are increasingly choosing their marriage partners for themselves.

Activity   Draw a flow chart to show all the good and bad things about arranged marriage.

When you are able to choose your partner for marriage, it is good to think about what qualities you value in a partner and what type of marriage you want before you choose. Then you can talk to each other about your ideas and agree on how you want to live together. This is better than finding out after marriage that you have very different dreams.

Some good questions to ask before marriage are:

- how you will share housework, childcare, farming and paid work between you;
- how you will both make, share and use money;
- how many children you want and when;
- how important religion is to each of you;
- where you will live;
- how involved you will be with your families and family responsibilities;
- if either of you have any health problems or behaviours related to health like heavy drinking or smoking.

In your personal lives, qualities such as respect, love, trust, faithfulness, gentleness and sexual attraction are often important.

Husbands and wives who are friends can talk together, listen to each other and work out ways to live happily together and solve problems.

1 Imagine that you are making an advertisement for a husband or wife. What qualities will you look for in your partner? How do you want to live together in your ideal marriage?

2 In small groups of boys or girls only, make pictures or role plays to present to the others that show your ideal partner and marriage. Do boys and girls have different ideas about the ideal partner and marriage? If so, talk about them together and see whether you can agree.

A happy sex life in marriage

Married couples can go on enjoying their sexual lives until old age if they care about each other and make time to be together. Try to keep the romance of the early days alive.

Sometimes, however, a couple's sex life is not so happy.

Husbands or wives may feel hurt if their partner has a lover or lovers outside their marriage. Infidelity can spoil a couple's sex life and cause worry about infections, particularly HIV. It is very important that men and woman practise safer sex if they have lovers outside marriage so that they do not infect their partners and children.

• Activities

1 Draw flow charts to show why husbands and wives might have lovers outside their marriage and what could help them to stay only with each other.

2 Talk with your parents or grandparents to learn from them how marriage and divorce has changed since they were young. What do they think are the good and bad things about these changes?

5 Looking after each other

In this chapter we look at some painful topics: sexual harassment, rape, sexual abuse, incest and violence. These things are hard to think about, but they do happen, especially to women and young people. If we can talk about them together, we may be able to find ways to avoid or cope with them; or to change our society so that relationships between men and women become more equal and caring.

Rape

What is rape?

Rape means a person forcing another person to have sexual intercourse against their will. Usually, it is a man who rapes a woman or another man. In this chapter we refer to rape happening to women, but remember that it can also happen to boys or men.

A rapist may force a woman to have sex by threatening to hurt or kill her, by beating her or by humiliating her.

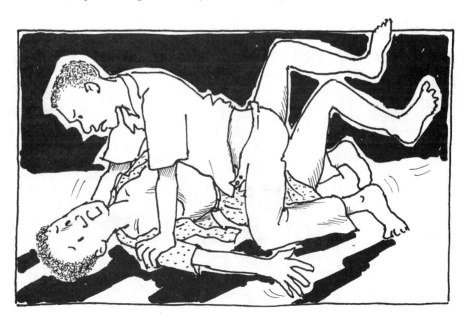

When might rape happen?

People are usually raped by someone they know, often in a familiar place. Rapes by strangers are rare.

Mariama aged 13 liked Kofi, a sixth form boy. He invited her out and bought her sweet wine. He took her to his home to meet his sister but no one was in. He started kissing her. At first she was happy but then his hands moved down her body and she said 'no' and struggled to get away. He did not take any notice and forced her to have sex with him.

Memuna was selling groundnuts around the town after dark. A man told her to come into the house while he found some money. He raped her.

Florence was alone in the house with her stepfather. She was in the bathroom when he came in and forced her to have sex with him.

Why do men rape?

Some boys may not think they have done anything wrong when they rape a girl. In many societies, girls are expected to say 'no' to sex and boys are expected to keep pushing the girls until they say 'yes'. These boys don't believe that when a girl says 'no' she means 'no'.

Boys and girls may believe that if a boy spends money on a girl, she owes him sex.

I have a right to sex with my wife any time I like — I paid for her.

Like an animal you mean? That's not right – women are human beings not animals.

Boys and girls may think that a boy's sexual needs are so strong that he cannot control himself – that he must have sex whether the girl wants it or not or he will be ill. The truth is that a boy can control his sexual urges without harm and should understand that when a girl says 'no', she means 'no'.

In many societies women have lower status than men. Men may think that they own women in the same way that they own animals. They believe that they have the right to have sex with them anytime they want it. They do not believe that a man can rape his wife.

A boy who is unloved or has been badly treated in life may rape girls to feel powerful or as revenge against people who have hurt him. He may see rape as a way to show that he is a man.

Some men become violent when they drink alcohol or take drugs.

In times of conflict and war, men often use rape as a weapon against the other side and use it to humiliate the losers and show that they have been defeated.

What can we do to prevent rape?

- If you are a boy or man, listen to what girls or women are saying. If they say 'no', cry or look unhappy, they do not want to have sex with you. Imagine how you would feel if you were forced to have sex. Think about the consequences of rape for the girl and yourself. Could you live with pregnancy, abortion, STDs, HIV, low self-esteem and fear?

- Boys and girls can act as equals. They can both be strong and responsible and make decisions together. Girls can make it clear that they are not going to exchange sex for a bottle of coke and boys can stop expecting this.

- Stay in places where there are lots of people. Don't get into cars, enter houses or go to the bush with a person who you don't know well or someone you know wants to have sex with you.

- Think about how you will get home if you are going out in the evening. Try to avoid walking alone in lonely places. If you have to walk alone, walk fast with your head up and shoulders back as if you are meeting someone. Carry an umbrella or stick.

You owe me– I bought you a coke.

Is that what you think I'm worth––a bottle of coke? GET LOST!

- If you are working at night or on the farm, try to work with a friend or in a group. Don't let anyone force you into his house, truck or to a lonely place.

- Boys and girls can both avoid drinking alcohol so that they are in control of things and can think clearly. Try to avoid places where men are drinking a lot.

- Girls, if you like a boy but don't want to have full sex with him, make this clear from the start. Boys, you are not animals. You can control your sexual urges and it will not harm you.

- Think about what you are wearing. If you are with your friends, it is OK to wear mini-skirts or sexy clothes. If you are walking home alone, it might be best to cover up with a chitenge. Boys, do not assume that a girl who is wearing a mini-skirt is asking for sex.

> World Human Rights say that everyone, whatever their age, sex or status has the right to freely decide on whether to engage in any sexual activity without violence or force.
>
> Rape is a criminal act. Rapists should be prosecuted and serve long prison sentences.

What to do if you think someone is going to rape you

Try to stay calm. If there are people about, scream and shout to bring help. The boy or man may stop or run away. Say assertively that you do not want to have sex. Tell him how you are feeling. He may put himself in your shoes and stop. If he does not, you could kick him hard in the testicles or squeeze his testicles hard. Then run away as fast as you can.

Penina's story

One day, I was walking home from the market at dusk and a man came up behind me and pushed me to the ground. I bit him on the cheek as hard as I could and he yelled and let me go. I jumped up and ran home as fast as I could. I was shaking and crying as I told my mother what had happened. She praised me for being strong and said that she would tell the police and elders to look out for a man with a bite on his face and arrest him. Next day they found him. He had been raping young girls for some time. I still have bad dreams about him but he is behind bars now. Everyone should know that rape is a criminal offence.

What to do if you have been raped

- Go to a safe place. Tell a friend or relative what happened.

- Check how rape cases are handled in your country and community. In some countries, the police will help you to bring the rapist to justice. If this is the case and you feel able to, go with your friend or relative and report the rape to the police. They will take a written statement about what happened. Do not wash yourself or change your clothes because they will want to have evidence. Take some other clothes with you in case they want to keep your clothes as proof that the rape took place. In some countries, visiting the police might be risky and cause you more distress because they are not trained to handle rape cases properly.

- The community may have ways of dealing with rape. Go with a friend or relative to report the rape to the community leaders.

- Go to a health worker and tell them what happened. They may be able to help you to prevent pregnancy and they can give you treatment for STDs. They can record any injuries you have and treat them. You may also want to have an HIV test after three months.

- If you are raped by someone you know, a boyfriend or relative or neighbour, do not keep it a secret. Remember you are not to blame and you can stop him from hurting someone else.

- Talk to someone about your feelings. Many girls feel unloved, dirty or angry after being raped. Talking about these feelings can help you to feel better.

Sexual abuse

What is sexual abuse?

Sexual abuse is when an adult makes sexual contact with a child or young person in a harmful and unwanted way. Sexual abuse can also happen between adults if one person is more powerful than another. For example an employer might abuse an employee. Refugees and prisoners are also at risk. Sexual abuse includes forced sex or rape; incest and sexual molesting.

Sexual molesting means unwanted sexual activities such as kissing or fondling the breasts or genitals (private parts).

Incest is sexual activity between a child and a parent or close relative. It is not right to engage in sexual activity with close family members.

Thandi's story

Every holiday, Thandi went to stay with her aunt and uncle in the city. When she was small, she liked her uncle. He was funny and carried her on his shoulders. When she was 12 years old, he started to touch her breasts and private parts in a way that made her feel very bad. He said it was their special secret and she mustn't tell anyone. She told her mother that she did not want to stay with her uncle again, but she could not say why. Her mother was annoyed and said she must not become a difficult teenager.

**Sexually abusing children is a crime.
A person found guilty of it
can go to prison.**

Sexual abuse is a big problem all over the world. Children are scared to talk about it. They think no-one will believe them or the abuser will hurt them. It is difficult for children to talk about sexual abuse because most children are abused by family members or people they know well.

What can you do about child sexual abuse?

If you feel upset, frightened or angry when someone touches you, you are being abused. This is true even if the person is your father or teacher, even if they say they love you and buy you nice things. You are a **child** and the person abusing you is an **adult**. He or she is always the one responsible for the abuse, it is **never** your fault. Do not feel ashamed or guilty.

You have the right to say 'no' to touches that you do not like, even from people you love. No-one has the right to touch you and ask you to keep that touch a secret. If someone touches you in a way which you do not like, say loudly 'Stop it, I do not like that, it is not right to touch children like that.' If someone asks you to touch him or her in a way you do not like, say the same thing.

Then tell someone who you trust what happened. If they don't believe you, find another person to tell. If you have been raped, go to see a health worker immediately.

Activity

Divide into four groups. Ask each group to discuss one of the stories in this chapter (Mariama, Memuna, Florence or Thandi's story).

- Who was responsible for what happened?
- How did each person feel?
- Why did each person behave as they did?
- What could each person have done to prevent the rape or abuse?
- What should each person do now?
- What help should other people give to prevent the rape or abuse?
- What help should other people give to the victim and the abuser now?

Violence

What kinds of violence happen in our community?

Violence includes slapping, kicking, beating, threatening, sexual abuse, humiliation, emotional abuse and murder. There are many kinds of abuse and one can lead to another. Violence can happen between sexual partners, children and parents, in-laws, siblings and school children. Young people, girls and women are most at risk of violence because people often have power over them.

Why do people use violence?

- People believe that they can get what they want through violence.
- People enjoy violence; it excites them.
- People believe that they have a right to hurt others because they have power over them.
- People believe that violence is the best way to make young people or women do what they want.
- People believe that violence is good for the one suffering it. Some people believe that if you 'Spare the rod, you spoil the child.' Or they believe the saying 'A wife, a dog and a walnut tree, the more you beat them, the better they be.'
- Men believe that violence proves their manhood.
- Men believe that women belong to them and violence is a way to keep them helpless, needy and afraid.
- People have grown up seeing violence used to solve problems. They do not know how to solve them any other way.

What are the harmful effects of violence?

Violence hurts those who suffer from it, their families and the whole community.

Activity   Draw a diagram to show the harmful effects of violence on young people, families and the community.

What can we do to stop the violence?

Violence carried out openly or in secret hurts the whole community. Young people can work with the community to change attitudes about violence and to protect everyone in the community.

You can help to stop violence by:

- talking about violence openly with friends, schoolmates and parents – making the problem visible and unacceptable;
- trying to get community leaders of all sorts to speak out against violence;
- helping to find peaceful ways to solve problems rather than fighting with each other;
  - helping boys to respect themselves, girls and women – making it clear that violence is not manly;
  - finding out about the legal system and how it protects people against violence of different sorts;
  - going to school and learning skills so that you can earn money without relying on parents or sexual partners;
- if you are in danger of violence, making a plan to help you stay safe or leave the violent situation;
- if you are beaten and hurt, telling a trusted person, for example, a relative, friend, health worker or teacher;
- if you suffer from violence at home, seeking help. Perhaps you could move to another relative's house.

• Activities

1 In groups of only boys and only girls, draw pictures to show the kinds of violence that young people suffer from in your community. Share your ideas together.

2 Is there a difference between the pictures drawn by boys and those drawn by girls? Do boys and girls have different ideas about what violence is?

3 For each of the kinds of violence, think of as many ideas as you can about how you could stop or cope with each kind of violence. What steps could you take at once to change things?

This is a difficult chapter because it is hard to think about rape, abuse and violence. However, if these problems are brought out in the open and everyone works together to change attitudes and behaviour, things can change.

6 | Children by choice, not chance

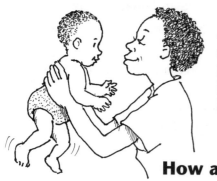

Children give pleasure, love and status and help a family to prosper. Having children is a very important part of our lives. In this chapter we look at how we can have children by choice so that mothers, fathers and children are healthy and live good lives.

How are babies made?

About 14 days before a girl's period starts, one of the ovaries releases a tiny egg. This egg travels along the Fallopian tube to the womb. If the girl has sex around the time when the egg is released, one of the sperm in the boy's semen may join with the egg to make a baby. The baby is planted in the rich lining of the womb and here it grows for nine months floating in a bag of liquid.

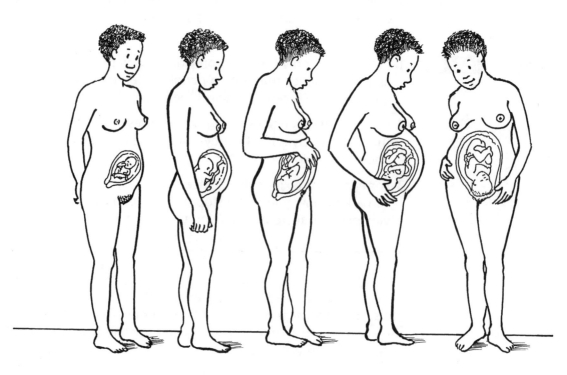

What are the signs of pregnancy?

The signs of pregnancy are:

- no period for six weeks or more;
- feeling like you are about to vomit, especially in the morning – this is called morning sickness;
- a bigger belly and breasts with dark areas around the nipples, belly and face;
- having to urinate often;
- history of recent sexual intercourse.

If you notice any of these signs, talk to a trusted person at once, especially if you did not plan to have a baby at this time. The earlier you know that you are pregnant and start to make decisions about it, the better the decisions will be.

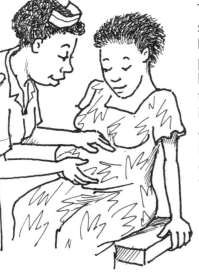

I'm glad you came - you are doing very well. Are you living with your mother?

Going to the antenatal clinic

The antenatal clinic looks after pregnant women so that childbearing is safer and healthier for both mother and child. It is very important that pregnant young girls attend the clinic regularly because childbearing is more risky for girls under the age of 18. The clinic will check that everything is going well, advise the girl about how to look after herself and give her an injection to protect her from tetanus. They may also advise her to deliver in hospital to make it safer for her and the baby.

Activity — Visit your local antenatal clinic and delivery ward.

- What might make it difficult for a pregnant teenager to attend the clinic?
- What would make it easier?

All about fertility

Girls are born with thousands of tiny unripe eggs in their ovaries. Boys release millions of sperm every time they ejaculate. It only takes one sperm to meet one egg to make a baby. This is why most people can make a baby very easily if they have sex when an egg is in the tube or womb.

However, some men and women find it difficult to make a baby. There are many reasons for this. The man may have too few sperm. The woman may not release eggs.

How can we protect our fertility as we are growing up?

- Protect yourself from STDs because they can block the woman's tubes so that the egg cannot pass to the womb for fertilisation. Say 'no' to sex or use condoms.

- Wait until you are at least 18 years before you have a pregnancy. Before this your body is not grown and your pelvis may be too small to let the baby out.

I was married at 13 and pregnant at 14. My baby could not come out. Now I can't have children, my urine leaks and I'm alone. Parents, let your girls grow to women before they marry or give birth.

- Avoid unsafe abortion (doing something to end a pregnancy) as this can cause an infection or damage to the organs. Say 'no' to sex or use contraceptives.

How can couples increase the likelihood of making a baby?

A woman and man who are trying to make a baby should: have sex at times when there is an egg in the tube or womb; not put herbs or powders in the vagina; not wash out the vagina after sex; not have too many 'rounds' of sex as this can weaken sperm; and try to eat well.

Having children by choice, not chance

African men and women have found ways to space their children so that the children are healthy and strong and the mother has time to rest. People have always known that children born too close together become malnourished. Couples avoided another pregnancy until the baby was weaned and walking. They prevented another pregnancy by breast-feeding for a long time and avoiding sex whilst breast-feeding. Sometimes the mother went to her mother's house for two years and the man took a second wife.

How is family planning changing?

• Activities

1 Talk to your parents or aunts about their choice of family planning. What local words do you know for family planning?

2 Talk to your grandparents about how they used to space children and the changes they see happening now.

Nowadays, many couples do not want to live apart to space their births. There are now new ways of preventing pregnancy that allow couples to enjoy sex all the time without worrying about pregnancy. These methods are called **contraceptives**. They allow couples to choose when to have a baby rather than leaving it to chance. They can plan to have babies at the best time for the mother, child, father and siblings.

Many people are choosing to have **fewer children**. They want to look after all their children's needs, send them to school and give them a good life. People need more cash but making a living is more difficult. Children are less likely to work on the farm and support their parents in old age.

Childbearing is safer for mother and child when:

- the mother is **at least 18 years old**;
- the **space** between children is **at least three years**;
- women have **no more than four children**;
- women have babies when they are **younger than 35 years old**;
- women **avoid unsafe abortion**.

A birth space of three years not only results in healthier babies, it also helps children to be intelligent and do well at school.

Ways to prevent pregnancy

• Activity

List some of the ways you know to prevent pregnancy.

What do you think are the good and bad things about each of the different ways?

> **You can't get pregnant if we do it standing up.**

> **That's nonsense!**

> **Don't listen to stories. Get the facts!**

There are lots of stories about how to avoid pregnancy.

You *can* get pregnant:

- the first time you have sex;
- if you have sex standing up;
- if you go to the toilet after sex;
- if you wash after sex;
- if the man withdraws his penis before coming;
- if you have sex during your period;
- if the boy is younger then 15 years;
- if the girl hasn't yet started her periods;
- if you have sex while breast-feeding a baby;
- if you don't use contraceptives correctly;
- if you have sex in the water.

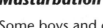

Saying 'no'

The safest way to avoid pregnancy is to say 'no' to sexual intercourse. You always have the right to say 'no' to sex. No matter who asks you, you have the right to say 'no!'.

> **I don't want to start sex till I'm older. I enjoy life with my friends and no hassle.**

Masturbation

Some boys and girls masturbate as a safe way of getting pleasure without putting themselves or anyone else at risk of pregnancy or STDs or HIV.

Enjoying yourself without sexual intercourse

Hugging, kissing, petting, stroking, dancing or caressing will not cause a pregnancy as long as you stop before intercourse. Mutual masturbation is when a couple play with each other's genitals. This is safe as long as no semen or vaginal fluid goes into the other person. People should wash their hands and cut their fingernails before masturbating.

It is your right to say what you want to do and how far you want to go in sex. You could say this at the start so that your partner knows what you want.

> I'm not ready for sex. I love cuddling and kissing and...

> ...talking about everything under the sun – I do too, so that's what we do.

Using a contraceptive

There are many different methods of contraception, each with their good points and bad points. People can choose the method that is best for them. People often change the method they use through their life as their needs change.

Many young people will not need this information until they are older and in a committed relationship. It is given here so that readers can use it when they need it.

Condoms

The male condom is a thin rubber tube that fits over the hard penis and catches the semen so that it cannot enter the vagina, anus or mouth. The condom acts as a tough extra skin that sperm, HIV and STD germs cannot get through. The female condom is made out of plastic and has a ring at each end. It is inserted into the vagina before intercourse. The rings keep it in place. Female condoms are now available in some countries.

> We choose condoms because they have no effect on the body.

> And they prevent pregnancy and HIV/STD.

> They're the best method for young people like us.

How to use a condom properly

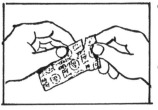

- Try to obtain your condoms from a shop or clinic that supplies many condoms and where they are stored in covered packages in a cool place out of the sun. If possible, check the expiry date.

- Check the condom package to make sure that there are no cracks, holes or open sides. If the colour of the condom is uneven or it is dry, brittle, torn or unusually sticky, throw it away because it will burst. Handle it carefully. Don't tear it with your fingernails.

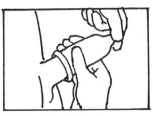

- Always put the condom on when the penis is hard, before having sex.

- Make sure that the condom is the right way up with the tip upwards and the roll on the outside. Pinch the tip of the condom with one hand. Do this to leave room for the semen so that the condom does not burst.

- Unroll the condom with the other hand, all the way down to the base of the penis, toward the body.

- The vagina and condom need to be wet to prevent the condom from breaking and to make sex more comfortable. A woman becomes wet when she is ready for sex. Be a good lover, take time to romance and caress your girlfriend so that she is wet. Many condoms have a special slippery oil on them. Some contain a chemical called nonoxynol 9 that kills sperm and some germs. For extra safety, the woman can use spermicide cream, foam or jelly in her vagina. Delfen foam is an example of a spermicidal foam.

- **Never** use vaseline, vegetable oil, mineral oil, hand lotion or anything made with oil to make condoms wet. Oil makes condoms burst.

- The couple can now enjoy themselves safely. The condom helps the man to go on longer so that the woman can reach orgasm.

- Condoms rarely break if they are used properly. If you feel the condom break, stop intercourse at once, remove the torn condom and apply another one.

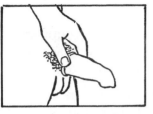

- After sex, while the penis is still hard, take the penis out by holding the rim of the condom with a tissue around the base of the penis so that the semen does not spill out or get on your hands.

- Take the condom off, wrap it up and dispose of it safely so that no child can play with it. Bury it, burn it or put it in the latrine. Do not use it again. Always use a new condom every time you have sex.

● **Activity**

Many people know about condoms but do not use them.

Make a drawing to show all the reasons why people don't use condoms. Look for ways to remove these barriers.

Talking about condoms

Young women and men may find it difficult to talk about using condoms.

● **Activity** In pairs, either mixed or separate boys and girls, do some role plays about different situations where two people are thinking about having sex together. Practise talking as young men and young women about condoms in these situations. For example, telling a new girlfriend that you want to use a condom; asking an older man to use a condom. (Point out that many people in the group may not be in a sexual relationship now but this activity helps you to be prepared for the future.)

Spermicides

Spermicides are creams, foams or jellies containing a chemical that kills sperm. Spermicides are put inside the vagina as foam with a special applicator or as tablets that the man or woman can push high into the vagina.

Spermicides are not very reliable by themselves. It is best to use them with condoms or a diaphragm.

Diaphragm

The diaphragm is a rubber cap that the woman puts into the vagina to cover the door to the womb. This stops the sperm from entering the womb to fertilise the egg.

The woman has to go to a health worker to get the correct size diaphragm for her and learn how to put it in properly.

The diaphragm is covered with spermicidal cream or jelly and then put into the vagina before having sex. It is left in for at least eight hours after sex.

The diaphragm may also protect the woman from some STDs and cancer of the cervix.

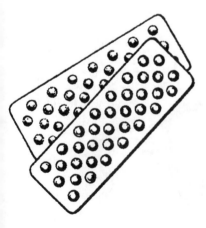

The Pill

The chemical or **hormone** in the pill stops the woman from releasing an egg each month so she cannot get pregnant. The hormone also changes the lining of the cervix and womb so that babies cannot develop there.

The woman takes **one pill every day**.

- The pill is very reliable.
- The pill makes periods lighter, more regular and less painful.
- When the woman wants to have a baby, she stops taking the pill and her body goes back to normal in a few months.
- The woman **must** remember to take the pill at the **same time every day**. If she forgets to take the pill for two days in a row she can get pregnant and should use a condom.

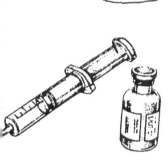

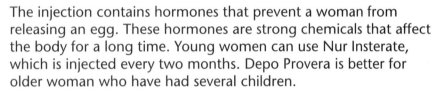

- The pill **does not protect against STDs and HIV.** You need to use **condoms** as well to protect against STDs and HIV.

  - Women should have their blood pressure checked if they take the pill because it can rise. If the woman smokes and takes the pill, she is more likely to have a stroke.

  - If the woman has diarrhoea or vomiting, she should use condoms for that month to give her extra protection.

  - The pill does not suit everyone. Some women get headaches, sore breasts, depression, weight gain, feel like vomiting or bleed lightly through the month. Often these problems go away after a few months.

The Injection – Depo Provera and Nur Insterate

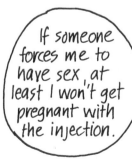

The injection contains hormones that prevent a woman from releasing an egg. These hormones are strong chemicals that affect the body for a long time. Young women can use Nur Insterate, which is injected every two months. Depo Provera is better for older woman who have had several children.

The injection does **not** protect against STDs or HIV. People at risk should use a condom as well.

- The method is very reliable at preventing pregnancy.
- No one need know that the woman is using a contraceptive.
- The woman only has to go to the clinic every two months.
- The injection changes the pattern of menstrual bleeding. Some women stop bleeding, some bleed very little and some bleed heavily.
- When the woman stops taking the injection she may not get pregnant again for a year or more.
- Some women put on weight.
- Some doctors do not like to give the injection to young girls.

The IUD or loop

The IUD is a small plastic object that is put into the womb by a doctor or nurse. It stops the egg and sperm meeting.

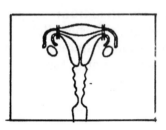

- The loop is a reliable contraceptive.
- The woman can keep the loop inside for five years.
- The woman can feel the thread that hangs into the vagina to check that the loop is still there.
- The loop does not interfere with sex.
- The loop can cause cramps and heavy or painful periods.
- The loop is not good for young women who have never had children.
- The loop does **not** protect against STDs or HIV. The loop increases the chances that a woman will get a serious infection that stops her from ever having children and makes her very ill.

Sterilisation

Sterilisation is an **operation** carried out on a man or a woman that stops them ever having children again. The tubes that carry the egg to the womb, or the sperm to the penis are cut. This is only done when the woman or man have had all the children they want and they are certain they do not want more.

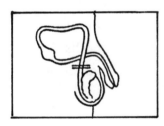

Natural family planning (NFP)

Women are only fertile for a few days each month when they release an egg. In NFP, the woman learns ways of knowing when she is fertile. She avoids sex at these times.

- NFP does not cost money.
- NFP has no harmful effects.
- It is natural.
- It is acceptable by the Church, especially Catholics.
- The man co-operates in the family planning by avoiding sex, using a condom or by sexual play without intercourse over the fertile time.
- The woman learns about her body.
- The couple have a rest from sex.

All women should learn to understand their monthly fertility cycle because this helps them to avoid pregnancy or to conceive.

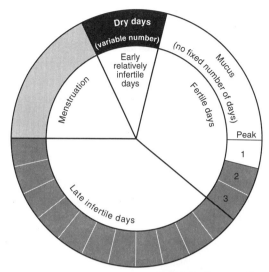

Teenagers often have irregular cycles at first. This makes it very difficult to know when a teenage girl is fertile and increases her chances of getting pregnant if she uses natural methods.

NFP is not as reliable as the pill, injection, IUD or condoms. It does not protect against STDs and HIV.

Withdrawal

Withdrawal is when the man takes his penis out of the vagina before he ejaculates. Withdrawal is **not a very good** method for preventing pregnancy because sperm can leak out of the penis before he ejaculates and he may not pull out in time. It takes skill for a man to pull out of the vagina before ejaculating. The woman has a one in three chance of falling pregnant using withdrawal.

• Activities

1 Draw a picture of all the contraceptives in this chapter to show the good points and problems with each for young people. Which ones do you prefer and why?

2 What makes it difficult for young people to use contraception?

3 What helps young people to use contraception?

4 Make a map to show where contraceptives, including condoms, are provided in your area.
   - What questions would you want to ask before you went to a place for contraception?
   - What are the good and bad points about all these sources of contraceptives?

5 Role-play explaining your needs to a nurse, community family planning agent or pharmacist.

6 Visit a family planning clinic or CBD agent.

Our ways did not always work but they were all we had in those days.

Using herbs

In many cultures herbs are used to avoid pregnancy or to bring on late periods. Women know about these herbs and teach their daughters about them. Some of these herbs may work and others may not work. Research is being done to find out how reliable and safe they are.

Using traditional methods

Some women use cultural methods to avoid pregnancy, for example a knotted string around the waist. Most women agree that these methods are not reliable and modern methods are more effective.

Emergency contraception

Some health services give special pills to prevent pregnancy to women who had sex within the last three days without using a contraceptive. Women should not use these pills as a method of contraception. They are **only** for emergencies.

Making decisions about pregnancy and contraception

Many young people (and older ones too!) become pregnant or get an STD or HIV because they have sex without thinking. One of the effects of sex is to reduce thinking and increase feeling. Knowing this, we can make our decisions before we get into a romantic or sexy situation.

The consequences of unplanned pregnancy are serious and so we must think before we have sex.

Men have always decided these things. Why should we change – it is our culture?

Yes, but women bear and raise the children, take the risk – they have a right to decide. It is their bodies!

What do you think?

1 Who should decide when to have babies and which method to use to prevent pregnancy?

2 Role-play a girlfriend and boyfriend or husband and wife talking about having babies and contraception.

Are you ready to have a child?

1 Carry an egg around with you for one week, everywhere you go. Imagine that this egg is your baby. You must look after the egg carefully so that it does not break or get too hot or cold. If you can't take the egg with you, you must find someone to look after it for you and pay or reward them in some way. Give your egg a name and a face. (If an egg is too costly or not available, look for something cheaper, perhaps a bag of flour.

- What did you think about looking after the egg? What were the good and bad things about it?

- How is looking after the egg like having a child? How is it different?

- What difference would it make to your life if you had a child now?

Remember, you only had to look after your egg for a week. A child is for life! Children need many more things than the egg.

2 Draw a spider diagram to show the good and bad things about having a child as an adolescent.

Why do teenagers have unplanned pregnancies? Who is responsible for teenage pregnancy?

Kalimi's story

I was 16 years old when I fell in love with Kaguti, my classmate. We kissed and petted but I refused to have sex with him because I was afraid of falling pregnant.

My family was having trouble paying my school fees. I felt bad. How could I help? One day, a businessman called Daniel asked me out. He gave me some money for my fees. He was funny and I enjoyed the nice hotel.

Kaguti and I were getting hot for each other. Kaguti promised that he would not get me pregnant. He tried to get condoms but the nurse said he was too young. He said that he would 'pull out' in time and I would not get pregnant. I didn't know anything about

sex, no-one talked to me about it. But Kaguti sounded as if he knew what he was doing. We had a nice time.

Next time Daniel took me to a different hotel, in the next town. He said we should rest in a bedroom. I did not want to play sex but he said I owed him. He gave me a pill so I would not get pregnant.

The next month, I did not see my period and I felt like vomiting all the time. I was pregnant.

Kaguti said that it could not be his baby because he pulled out in time. His friend had seen me with Daniel so it must have been him.

Daniel was very angry and said the baby was nothing to do with him! – hadn't I taken the pill? He said I am a prostitute and one of my other boyfriends made me pregnant.

What am I going to do?

● Activities

1 Draw a picture to show all the reasons why Kalimi got pregnant.

2 Which people in the story have some responsibility for Kalimi's problem?

3 Role-play scenes from the story with your ideas on how Kalimi, Kaguti and Daniel or the nurse could have acted differently so that Kalimi did not get pregnant.

4 What choices does Kalimi have now?

What are the choices for Kalimi?

She could have an abortion to end the pregnancy
Health services know how to carry out safe abortions in these ways.

- Medicines are put in the vagina and taken by mouth and this brings on the period.
- The tiny baby is sucked out of the womb with a vacuum tube very early in pregnancy.
- The womb is scraped clean to remove the baby.
- The girl is given drugs, which cause her to go into labour and she delivers the tiny baby.

What does the law say about abortion in your country?

In some countries abortion is legal for anyone who asks for it, or if continuing the pregnancy will harm the mother or baby. Sometimes abortion is only legal in cases of rape, incest or if the baby is severely handicapped. In other countries abortion is illegal in all cases.

Even if abortion is legal, it may still be difficult to obtain a safe abortion because of the high cost and delays. Many young girls have an unsafe abortion. The girl may drink poisons or herbs recommended by her friends or relatives. She may insert a twig or sharp object into her womb. This can tear the womb and leave the girl unable to have children.

Every year, many young girls die or are permanently injured and unable to have children because of unsafe abortions.

Abortion is safer if:

- it is carried out as soon after missing a period as possible, and not later than three months after missing a period;
- it is carried out by a qualified practitioner under sterile conditions;
- the girl goes to a health worker at once if she has continuous bleeding, smelly discharge, pain in the lower belly or fever and chills.

Kalimi could bring up her baby

Many girls go on with the pregnancy and do their best to bring up their babies with or without the father.

Kalimi or her family could ask another person to bring up her baby

Some girls give their babies to another person to look after, often a relative. The baby's well being will depend on the lifestyle of the new family and how much love and care the new 'mother' can provide.

1 Draw a picture to show the people you would ask for help if you became pregnant. Why did you choose these people?

2 Use the decision-making skills that you learnt in Chapter 3 to decide what you would do if you were Kalimi.

3 What do you think are the good and bad points of the three choices Kalimi has?

4 What questions do you need to think about to make your decision?

5 If you decided to keep your baby, what would you need?

Making a decision

Imagine you are Kalimi. What questions will you and those helping you need to think about in making a decision?

● How old am I and how will it affect my health and safety if I have a baby?

● What support can I expect from the father of the baby? Do I want to continue my relationship with him?

● What support can I expect from my family and friends? Can they help me to bring up the child?

● What resources do I and my supporters have to enable me to bring up my child well?

● What are my future plans for education and work? How will having a baby affect my plans and future?

● Can I obtain a safe abortion before I have been pregnant for three months?

● What are my own feelings about abortion?

Points of view

'I was doing well at school when I fell pregnant. I planned to become a teacher. But I had to leave all that and go back to the farm. My boyfriend went to university and now he is marrying a classmate with no baby. I don't wish this fate on anyone. Adults should teach us about sex and help us to protect ourselves.'

'I am determined to bring up my baby well. I cook food for sale where I can have him with me and I am planning to sell dresses. I don't need a man to help me, they are more of a trouble than a help anyway.'

'I think that all women have the right to contraceptives and safe abortion services. They have a human right to life and too many are dying from 'unsafe motherhood' while the men who impregnate them make the laws.'

'I am Kalimi's auntie. We have never had children, my husband didn't have enough sperm. It was very hard because people called me a witch. But we stuck together and I am now doing well in business.

I want to raise her baby and give it all the love that I have to give. We have enough money to give it a good start in life and Kalimi can go on with her studies. I wish I had thought to pay her fees before this crisis.'

'My friends and I used to be really scared of the sugar daddies in big cars who parked outside school to pick us up. They were our elders. How could we refuse them, even if we didn't need their money? Then one of our friends got pregnant and then we didn't see the car outside school again. We were very angry that he had done that to our friend. We decided to make a drama to show at the PTA community meeting. We depicted exactly what the sugar daddies do and the consequences for the girls. We showed a scene where a girl refused to go with a sugar daddy. Then we requested the whole community to stop the sugar daddies molesting our young girls this way. They know who they are and they should stop. We also requested a field where we could grow vegetables and earn some money for ourselves.'

7 | Sexually transmitted diseases

Can you get diseases from sex?

We all suffer from colds, diarrhoea or malaria. A cold is spread by sneezing, diarrhoea by dirty food or water and malaria by mosquitoes. Germs are carried from one sick person to infect another person who also gets sick.

Illnesses may also spread from person to person during sex. These are called Sexually Transmitted Diseases or STDs. If a boy or girl has an STD, some of the germs in his or her body go into their partner's body during sex.

What diseases do you know which people get through sex?

There are many different diseases passed through sex. Gonorrhoea, syphilis, herpes, chlamydia, warts and chancroid are common ones. AIDS is a new STD and HIV is the virus which causes AIDS.

How do you know if you have an STD?

Many people show no signs of illness at first. The person feels healthy, but the STD germs are inside his or her body injuring their reproductive organs. The person can pass an STD to someone else without knowing it.

Men often have signs of an STD earlier than women.

Some signs of an STD

- Sores on the sex parts, lips or anus that may be very painful (chancroid) or painless (syphilis). There may be one sore or many. Sometimes the glands in the groin swell up and the sores may burst.
- Some STDs (for example, gonorrhoea) cause liquid to come from the penis or vagina. This is called a discharge.
- Men with gonorrhoea may have a burning pain when they urinate and a white or yellow discharge from the penis.

- Signs of STDs in women are an unusual white, yellow or greenish discharge, which may smell bad. The sex parts may itch, burn or feel sore. A woman may have a pain in her lower belly, backache, fever and chills.

Visit a health worker at once if you have lower belly pain, fever and chills.

- It is normal for women to have some whitish, nice smelling discharge from the vagina. This changes through the menstrual cycle.

- When women are sexually aroused, the vagina becomes wet. This is normal, it does not mean that the girl has a disease or has many partners. The wetness helps to make sex comfortable and prevent damage to the vagina.

- Some unusual discharges in women are **not** signs of an STD. Women may get an infection called **thrush** that is not sexually transmitted. This causes a white, thick discharge and itching, sore genitals. They may get germs in their sex parts when wiping the anus, from working in dirty water or from towels or cloths used in menstruation. Girls should always wipe the anus from front to back.

A less serious STD that causes itching is pubic lice. These are tiny insects that live in the pubic hair and go from one person to another during sex. A special lotion kills them.

AIDS is a new STD caused by the HIV virus. A person with HIV may have no symptoms for many years but can still infect others without knowing it.

Are STDs dangerous?

STDs can have serious consequences:

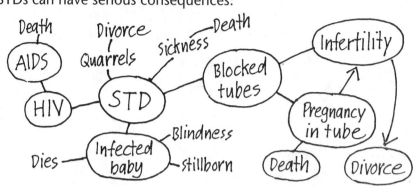

Protect your fertility and your unborn children. Protect yourself from STDs.

Daniel's story

When I was 19, I fell in love with Kiki and we became lovers. We were happy together but one day I had to go to town to arrange some business. In the evening, I had a drink or two with a colleague and we got chatting to a couple of beautiful girls. Somehow or other, I landed up in bed with one of them. A few days later, I had a burning pain when I urinated and a discharge. It was gonorrhoea. I took some herbs and made excuses not to have sex for a few days. I didn't tell Kiki about it. I thought that I would tell her if she got sick but she seemed fine. Then one day, she was very ill. She had bad pain in the bottom of her belly, fever and shaking. I took her to the clinic. They said that she had Pelvic Inflammatory Disease, probably caused by gonorrhoea. They told me that this could make a woman infertile. I felt really terrible. I had done this to her. We had decided to marry and I had put our children at risk.

• Activities

1 Role-play Daniel's story. Role-play different endings to it.

2 Role-play the story from the beginning so that it ends happily.

Who can get an STD?

STDs can infect anyone who has sex with a person who has an STD. Male or female, young or old, married or single, at school or out of school, rich or poor, farmers or businessmen, they can all get STDs.

Women get STDs and HIV from men twice as easily as men from women. A girl's organs are still growing and easily attacked by germs. The germs in the semen stay inside the vagina for a long time whereas men can easily wash germs from the vagina off the penis.

How can have an TD when only had sex with you?

... and I only had sex once with another girl – sorry.

People do not become infected every time they have sex with a person with an STD or HIV. It is like a lottery, you may win or lose. Even if you have had sex before, you may still be free of STDs or HIV. Protect yourself from now on! But remember you can get HIV or an STD the first time you have sex. So be prepared to protect yourself now even if you do not intend to have sex until you are older. Obtain some condoms beforehand if you are thinking about having sex.

What should I do if I think I may have an STD?

People often try several treatments to cure STDs. Some of these stop the signs of illness but do not kill the germs. The germs continue to harm the body and infect other people.

- You **cannot** cure an STD or HIV by having sex with a virgin (girl who has not had sex before). You will still have the germs in your body after sex and you will probably have infected the virgin as well.

- Some herbs can treat STDs but they may not kill all the STD germs. Then there is a danger that you remain infected without knowing it.

- Talk to a trusted person. A spiritual healer may help you to feel better but he cannot kill the STD germs.

- **It is important to go at once to see a doctor or nurse** if you have any signs of an STD. They will give you treatment to kill all the germs so that you are completely cured. This will protect your fertility and health.

- You must finish all the medicine even if you feel better. Otherwise some of the germs will stay in your body and make you ill later on. Also, you can still infect other people. Avoid alcohol during treatment.

- You must tell all your sexual partners to go for treatment. Otherwise they may get very sick and be unable to have children. Many people do not have any signs of illness, so your information may save their life or their fertility.

I'm so glad he told me to go to the clinic. These diseases can stop you even having children.

He's a good friend. I really admire boys who care about their girls.

Get proper treatment quickly!

- Do not have sex until you are cured. Otherwise you will pass the germs to your partner and they will infect you again.

- REMEMBER: HIV passes more easily into a man or woman who has sores or discharges from an untreated STD.

Get proper treatment quickly!

● Activities

1 Who would you go to for help if you had signs of an STD?

2 Draw a community map to show all the places where you could get help for an STD. What makes it difficult for young men and women to use these services? What could make it easier?

3 Role-play telling your partner that you have an STD and that he or she should go for treatment.

What is AIDS?

AIDS is a sickness caused by a virus called Human Immuno-deficiency Virus or HIV. AIDS stands for Acquired Immune Deficiency Syndrome. HIV attacks our body's defences against sickness, which are called our immune system.

HIV behaves like termites in a house. At first, the viruses hide inside the white blood cells and multiply. Nobody realises that anything is wrong. At this stage you are HIV positive but you do not have AIDS.

After a number of years a person with HIV starts to get sicknesses such as swollen glands, weight loss, frequent fever, diarrhoea, cough and skin problems. This happens because the immune system is weak.

As time goes on, the person get serious illnesses in the lungs, brain or gut and they now have AIDS. At present most people with AIDS eventually die. However, many people with HIV live for many years before they get sick and die.

How is HIV spread?

HIV is only found in large enough amounts to infect another person in four liquids: blood, semen, vaginal fluids and breast milk. HIV is not found in the air. It dies quickly when it is dried, heated or in contact with bleach or acid. Saliva, tears and sweat do not contain enough HIV to infect another person. Also these liquids contain a lot of antibodies to protect the body.

The HIV in blood, semen or vaginal fluid has to get inside the body of another person and into their bloodstream. This can only happen in the following ways:

Through sex

HIV is spread mostly through sex between men and women. It is also spread during sex between two men or two women.

Through blood

If blood is taken from a person with HIV and transfused (put) into another person, that person will also get HIV. In many hospitals blood is tested for HIV and thrown away if it is infected. One way to get HIV free blood is to ask relatives at low risk of having HIV to donate blood.

● Activities

1 Visit a health centre or a hospital and ask the nurses how they protect patients from HIV in blood transfusions and injections.

2 Who would you choose to donate blood if you needed a blood transfusion?

3 How could you avoid having blood transfusions?

Through unsterilised equipment

HIV can pass from one person to another on needles or razors that are not sterilised each time they are used. People who inject drugs often get HIV for this reason. Health workers are trained to use sterile equipment so this is much safer. Traditional healers should use new razors for cutting or sterilise their knives by soaking them in bleach or boiling them.

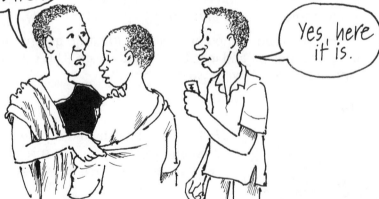

● Activities

1 What local customs might spread HIV through blood?

2 What can you do to protect yourself from HIV if you go to a traditional healer, village health worker, health centre or hospital?

I'm never going to have sex without a condom. Imagine giving AIDS to your baby!

I'm not even going to have sex now. Romancing and cuddling is enough for me.

From mother to baby

HIV from an infected mother can enter a baby in the womb, during delivery or during breast-feeding. About one in three babies of HIV positive mothers get HIV. These children usually develop AIDS and die within a few years. Mothers can reduce the risk of HIV in their babies by using condoms over the period of pregnancy and breast-feeding and seeking advice on the safest form of delivery.

About one in ten babies of mothers with HIV become infected through breast-feeding. In homes where there is no clean water supply or money for plenty of cow's milk, mothers should continue to breast-feed their babies even if they have HIV. Otherwise they may die of malnutrition and diarrhoea.

● Activity   What can boys and girls do to protect their future children from AIDS?

How HIV is not spread

HIV is only found in blood, semen and vaginal fluid and has to get inside the body and blood of another person to spread. This is why HIV does not spread through kissing, hugging, holding hands, sharing toilets, going to school together, sharing clothes, food or drink, sneezing and coughing or mosquitoes.

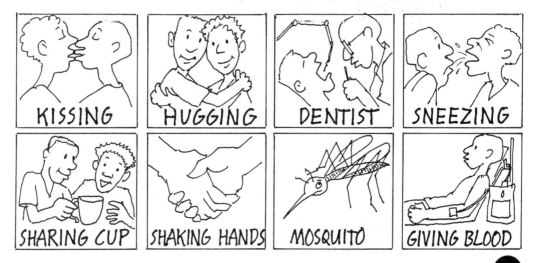

KISSING   HUGGING   DENTIST   SNEEZING

SHARING CUP   SHAKING HANDS   MOSQUITO   GIVING BLOOD

It's good to know it's never too late to change!

It is perfectly safe to live, laugh, eat, go to school and work with people with HIV and AIDS.

Some people believe that you can protect yourself from HIV by avoiding sex with certain types of people. For example, by avoiding sex with a woman who has had an abortion. It is true that a woman who has had an abortion has had sex without a condom, and therefore might be at risk of HIV. But the same is true of every other woman and man who has had sex without a condom.

How can I protect myself from STDs and AIDS?

Many people who have had sex believe that they already have HIV infection and believe that there is no point in practising safer sex. The truth is the majority of boys and girls who have had sex are still free of HIV. By practising safer sex from now on, you have a good chance of a healthy future with a family and children.

- You cannot protect yourself by choosing a healthy looking partner. Many people have no symptoms of an STD. A person with HIV may have no signs at all for many years but can still infect you without knowing it.

Let's wait until we are older and know each other better.

OK but let's talk about how we can love each other safely as well.

  - Say 'no' to sex. This is 100 per cent safe sex. Wait until you are older and you are in a caring relationship where you can discuss safer sex.

  - If you have sex, stay with the same partner. The more partners you have, the higher the risk that one of them will have HIV. This is true whether you have two partners at the same time or one partner for some time and them change to a new partner for some time.

- Many people believe that they are not at risk of HIV or an STD if they only have sex with one 'trusted' boy or girl for some time and then change to another partner who they also stick with. Some feel that their partner is a 'good' person who would not have HIV. Unfortunately, a person only has to have one partner who had HIV before meeting you to catch HIV without knowing it.

These bad boys come asking for condoms - I send them packing!

BOB MARLEY

I think they are behaving responsibly - we used to do without condoms, that's bad!

- Always use a condom when you have sex unless you *know* that you and your partner do not have an STD or HIV. Condoms also prevent pregnancy so they are a very good method for young people. They are not 100 per cent safe because they can break.

- You can show love by kissing, rubbing against each other, sensual massage, dancing, caressing, cuddling and touching each other's sex parts. These are all safe as long as semen or vaginal fluid does not get onto the other persons' sex parts.

- Masturbation by yourself is safe and some boys and girls masturbate to cope with their sexual feelings.

- Withdrawal is not safe because often some liquid comes out of the penis before ejaculation and this may contain HIV. Also, women are putting their lives in the hands of men and their skill in withdrawing.

- Oral sex is when people kiss, lick or suck each other's sex parts with the mouth. This has a lower risk of HIV infection than sexual intercourse. It is safer if the boy wears a condom and people do not have any sores in the mouth.

- Anal sex is risky because the lining of the rectum is easily torn and HIV can pass through. Use plenty of lubricants with condoms.

What are the good things and the problems with these different ways of protecting yourself from STDs and AIDS?

There are good things and difficult things about all these choices. Different choices suit people at different times of their lives. Talk about the choices with a small group of friends or peers. Then you can find ways to help each other to protect yourselves from STDs and HIV.

• Activities

1 In groups of only boys and only girls, talk about the good points and difficulties with each option.

2 Role-play some of the situations that might lead to unsafe sex. In each role play, ask: What are the reasons why the boy and girl had unsafe sex?

3 Now repeat the role play showing how they could abstain or have safe sex.

4 Show the role plays to the other group.

5 What would make it easier for girls and boys to protect themselves from STDs and HIV?

Letter page

• •

Dear Auntie Bea

My church says that sex outside marriage is sinful. My teacher says we should not have sex until we marry because we will get AIDS. But it seems to me that boys can have sex as much as they like. The village people say girls need the boys' water to grow into beautiful women. My girlfriends who have sugar daddies dress much better than I do and my mother is complaining that I don't bring any money home. I feel very confused about what to do. I know that HIV stays in the body for ever. So what is the point of keeping away from sex now when I will probably get HIV from my husband on my wedding night? We girls have no control over sex, we have to do what the boys say – what can I do?

Worried,
Agnes

1 Read the letter out to the class and ask girls and boys in small groups to respond to Agnes. This could be done as a role play, with one person acting as Agnes and the rest of the group as her advisors.

2 Alternatively do a role play using the different characters in the story.

3 How can girls take more control over their lives?

4 How can boys respect and value girls as equals?

I'm going to keep away from sex until I marry. Then you can marry me Agnes!

We'll have an HIV test before we marry. No test—no marriage!

That's a bit tough! I use a condom.

What is the HIV antibody test and how can it help?

Some hospitals test blood to see if it contains antibodies (chemicals that the body makes to fight germs) to HIV. They look for antibodies because six weeks after HIV enters the body, the body makes antibodies to fight the HIV. If the test is positive, it means that the person has HIV in their body. It does not mean that they have AIDS.

If you want to have an HIV test you should wait for three months after risky sex because there won't be enough antibodies to show up on the test until then.

1 Find out about HIV testing services in your district.

2 Imagine that you are thinking about having an HIV test.

3 What would you want to know and think about before having the test?

4 What advantages and disadvantages can you see in having a test?

Points of view

'I'd had sex before and I was sure I had HIV so I didn't care about anything. Then I had an HIV test and found I don't have HIV. I'm so happy. I will never risk HIV again. I'm planning for a future I never thought I'd have.'

'I would never have an HIV test. Supposing it said you have HIV? Everyone would talk badly about you and your family. I would kill myself.'

'My sister had an HIV test and found that she has HIV. At first she was very upset but we all helped her to cope and she is still fine. She teaches the young ones to protect themselves from AIDS and they really listen to her. She eats well and says that she won't have a boyfriend unless she meets someone really special who will understand her.'

Worries about family and friends

Many young people are worried that their parents will get AIDS and die, leaving them as orphans with no money for food and schooling and younger siblings to look after. Some fathers have lovers outside marriage. Their children worry that they will give HIV to their mother and both parents will die.

Maybe if young people could talk about these worries to their parents, they would try to protect themselves from HIV too.

I feel really worried when I see fathers going to the bar with other women. I wish all fathers and mothers would think about AIDS.

How can we help people with HIV infection?

If we can think and talk of people 'living with HIV infection' rather than 'dying of AIDS' it helps to reduce fear and makes people more hopeful about the future.

People with HIV can live normal lives for as long as possible if they:

- practise safer sex to avoid getting more HIV into their bodies;

- eat well, avoid too much alcohol and tobacco and avoid stress;

- get treatment for their infections as early as possible;

- carry on working as normal;

- get love and care from people around them.

They can protect others by using condoms and not donating blood.

If you are caring for someone with AIDS:

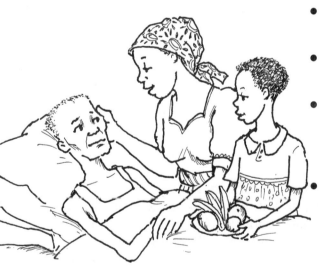

- Help them to stay healthy in the ways suggested above.

- Encourage them to talk openly about their feelings, listen and empathise.

- Care for them at home except when they have a bad infection. Do not isolate them because the virus is not spread through air or touch.

- Boil bloodstained clothes or soak them in bleach. Use plastic gloves or bags over your hands if you are cleaning blood, wounds or bloody diarrhoea. Wash your hands frequently and cover any sores or cuts.

- Seek advice for symptoms and treat them early.

Divide into groups of ten. First decide for yourself whether each of the statements in the quiz below is true or false. Then discuss them one by one in your group.

Quiz: What do you know about STDs?

Answer True or False.

1 STDs can make a woman unable to have babies.
2 You can get cured of STDs and AIDS by having sex with a virgin.
3 You cannot always tell that a person has an STD by looking.
4 You cannot get HIV the first time you have sex.
5 Condoms protect men and women against STDs.
6 You can get HIV by having sex with a woman who has had an abortion.
7 If a woman is taking the pill, there is no need to use a condom.
8 If you do not take all your medicines, you will continue to have an STD.
9 STDs go twice as easily from men to women than from women to men.

We have reached the end of the chapter on Sexually Transmitted Diseases. These are dangerous diseases so it is important to protect yourself and your unborn children by thinking carefully about which safer sex choice is best for you. Remember that abstinence is the only choice that is 100 per cent safe.

8 | Keeping ourselves healthy

There are things that we can do to help our bodies stay healthy. We can eat nutritious foods, take enough rest and exercise, reduce stress and avoid drinking too much, smoking or taking drugs. Sometimes our living situations make it difficult to follow healthy habits. But if we understand the reasons why we behave as we do, we may find ways to look after our health or change the things that affect our health.

Using drugs

In this chapter we are talking about those substances which people use to change the way that they feel or think, for example, alcohol, tobacco or marijuana. In small quantities, drugs make people feel happy, confident, relaxed, imaginative or energetic. If too much of the drug is taken or it is taken too frequently, people begin to have bad feelings and lose control of their actions.

One important step we can take is to say 'no' to drugs such as alcohol, cigarettes and marijuana. It is easier to avoid these substances than to give them up once we have grown to need them. If we can't avoid them, it is important to use them sensibly. Some people use drugs only at certain times when they are relaxing or at social events. They do not miss the drugs when they do not use them.

Some people misuse drugs. They lose control over when they use them, how much they use and the way that they behave when they are using them. When a person's mind feels a great need for a drug, it is called **dependence**. When a person's body feels such a strong need for a drug that they get sick without it, it is called **addiction**.

Let's look at each substance one by one.

Alcohol

What alcoholic drinks do people take in your community?

All alcoholic drinks contain pure ethanol in varying amounts. The strength of alcoholic drinks in bottles or cans is shown by a number followed by alcohol % volume or %vol or %ABV.

These drinks all contain the same amount of alcohol

Tot of spirit (Gin, whisky, local spirits)

small glass of wine (Palmwine depends on stage of fermentation)

½ pint of beer (Local beer-depends on length of fermentation)

¼ pint of strong beer

Locally brewed beer and distilled spirits may be much stronger than the bottled ones. They may also contain methanol, which is poisonous and can cause blindness.

Alcohol goes into the blood within a few minutes of being drunk and is carried to all parts of the body. It stays in the body for many hours before the liver breaks down all the alcohol.

People get drunk more quickly if they:

- are not yet mature and are small and light;
- are female;
- drink strong drinks;
- drink quickly;
- are not used to drinking alcohol;
- drink only without eating solids.

Alcohol causes people to lose their co-ordination; become slow to react to situations and make poor decisions.

People who are drunk are more likely to have an accident, get into arguments or do something stupid. They may vomit, lose consciousness or forget what happened to them. Many girls are pushed into sex they do not want when they drink alcohol or use drugs. This may result in unwanted pregnancy, STDs or HIV/AIDS.

Alcohol (and drugs) used during pregnancy can cause children to be born with birth defects and mental disabilities.

Is drinking a problem for young people in our community?

Charity's story

I started to drink sweet wine with my first boyfriend. I felt more confident and forgot my problems for a while. I didn't notice that I was drinking two glasses and then three. As soon as he filled my glass, I would drink it, faster and faster. The next day, I often had a really bad headache and vomited. I made excuses to stay off school. Then one day, I woke up in bed with a boy I hardly knew. I could not remember how I got there or what happened. Another boy came in and they both laughed at me and asked if I remembered the strip-tease? I was so ashamed and frightened. Who saw me? Did I have sex? Am I pregnant or infected with HIV? I realised then that I have a drink problem.

What can I do?

Activities

1 What are the warning signs that show that Charity was drinking too much?

2 Look at your own drinking behaviour. Do you have any of the warning signs?

3 What help could you give to Charity? How can you help friends who have a drink problem?

4 Do some role plays to show situations where young people drink too much alcohol. What caused them to drink too much?

5 Now replay the role plays, this time with the young people either not drinking at all or drinking sensibly. What helped them to avoid getting drunk?

6 What are the good things about not getting drunk?

Some good reasons for not getting drunk!

- People will respect and admire the 'real' you more than the 'drunk' you.
- You'll get home safely and remember the journey.
- You'll be able to make good decisions about sex and safety.
- You won't suffer from vomiting, headache and a hangover.
- You will be able to have a good conversation with people you like and will remember it the next day.
- You'll be able to perform better at school or work.
- You'll feel and look better.
- You'll be fitter and do better at sports.
- You'll save money.

Tips for avoiding alcohol altogether or drinking less

- Practise saying 'no'.
- Watch out for people who put strong drink or drugs into your soft drink. Some people think that this is funny but it can be very dangerous.
- Say that your religion forbids you to drink or you have something really important to do the next day.
- Say that you don't like the taste of alcohol.
- Say that it is against the law to drink at your age.

If you already drink alcohol and want to drink less:

- Decide beforehand how much you are going to drink in an evening and try to keep to it.
- Keep a note of how much you drink, on what occasions you drink and who you were with. Can you see what 'triggers' you to drink too much and why?
- Drink less strong drinks mixed with soft drinks like Coke or Sprite. (But remember they still contain alcohol.)
- Drink slowly and don't let people fill up your glass.
- Drink soft drinks on a day when you would drink alcohol.

Overcoming a drink or drug problem

If you have a drink or drug problem, you can overcome it if you want to stop. Then you need to learn to live without misusing drink or drugs. There are four stages to stopping:

1 Admit that you have a problem.

2 Decide to do something **today**, not tomorrow.

3 Stop or use less and then stop.

4 If you start again, don't blame yourself. Try to stop again right away.

It helps if your friends and family support you while you are stopping. If a group of friends decide to stop together, they can give each other strength.

Some people get sick for a few days when they stop drinking. They might shake, sweat, ache, vomit, feel irritable and have trouble eating and sleeping. Usually these feelings go away by themselves. Sometimes a person gets very ill and needs to go to the health centre. Try to eat lots of good foods to heal your body. See page 110.

Learning to stay free of alcohol or drugs or to use them sensibly

Try the tips for avoiding getting drunk on page 104. Try to relax and have fun in places where people do not drink or use drugs. Meet with friends who are also trying not to get drunk or have decided not to use drugs.

Alcohol and adults

Some children have a parent or parents who drink too much alcohol. This is very worrying because they may be violent, irresponsible and spend scarce money needed for the welfare of the family.

Look at the pictures that some children in Zimbabwe drew to show the impact of a drunken father in the home.

Impact diagram

A. Father drunk
B. Father going to field
C. Father cooking a chicken
D. House, no millie meal
E. Drunk father beating son
F. The way to the drinking
G. Father stealing money at home
H. Burning house
L. A drunk father beating the mother
M. Daughter is cooking
N. Mother going back to parents home
O. Hungry child, nothing to do
Q. Father throwing away food

What can you do if one of your parents or relatives has a drink problem?

- Talk to your other relatives and elders.
- Try to form a support group with friends who have the same problem. Talk about your problems with these friends and look for solutions.
- Find out about women's support groups and help women with violent partners.
- Do not blame yourself for your relative's problem.
- Perform a drama to the community that shows the impact of a parent or parents with a drink problem on their children.
- Do not get into the vehicle of anyone who has been drinking. You could be killed in a road accident or they could kill someone else.

Smoking cigarettes

The chemicals in cigarettes are extremely bad for your health. That is why cigarette packets carry a health warning. Isn't it odd to pay money for something that informs you that it can kill you?

Cigarettes contain a drug called nicotine that gives smokers a buzz. It also makes your veins and arteries narrow and causes high blood pressure and heart disease. The tobacco contains tar, which stops your lungs cleaning themselves properly so that you get more lung infections. Tar causes cancer of the lungs and throat.

Smoking takes away oxygen from your body so that it cannot work as well. It also ages your skin and damages unborn babies.

Smoking not only harms the people who smoke. It damages those around them as well because they have to breathe in the poisonous fumes.

Activities

1 Why do young people like you start smoking in your community?

2 What are the good things and bad things about smoking?

3 Practise saying 'no' to smoking in role plays.

Other drugs

Cannabis (dagga, marijuana, grass)

Cannabis, like tobacco, is a leaf that contains a drug and is smoked or eaten as hashish. Cannabis often makes users feel peaceful, lazy, friendly and like laughing. It does not cause the same problems as tobacco, but some people like it so much that they smoke it a lot of the time. This can make it difficult for them to concentrate at school and work and they may have accidents. A few people seem to get mental problems after smoking cannabis very frequently.

As cannabis is illegal in most countries, people who smoke it put themselves at risk of going to prison or being heavily fined.

Glue and solvent sniffing

Sniffing glue or solvents makes people feel 'high' for a time. However, this is very addictive and can cause problems with seeing, thinking and remembering, violent behaviour, loss of judgement and body control and death.

Heroin and cocaine

These two drugs are very addictive. They are said to make the user feel so good that they want to take them again and will do anything to get enough money to buy more. They may steal from their parents or outside to pay for their habit. Heroin and cocaine are dangerous drugs and many people die from using them. If they are injected, there is a risk of getting HIV if the needles are not sterilised.

Say 'NO' to hard drugs. Anyone found using or selling drugs can be sent to prison so it is best to say 'NO' to these drugs.

Ecstasy and other drugs

Young people can now buy drugs that make them feel happy and energetic for a whole night. Ecstasy is an example of this. The main problem with ecstasy is that it is new and people have not been taking it for long enough to know the long-term side effects. It may damage the brain and cause memory loss and other problems. It is important to drink water and not alcohol with ecstasy as some young people have died of dehydration after dancing all night without drinking water.

Miraa

Miraa is the leaf of a bush that contains a stimulating drug like cola. The leaves are chewed and the user is able to stay awake and active for many hours without eating or resting. However, users find it difficult to sleep and long term use can result in stomach problems, constipation, inability to get an erection and disharmony at home.

Which drugs are used in your community and what are the good and bad points of each?

The types of drugs used and the ways in which they are used vary greatly from place to place.

Using drugs has good and bad points for individuals and communities. Miraa and beer brewing bring in money for many families. A calabash of beer helps people to make friends or work hard in the fields. At the same time, some people misuse these drugs, with damaging effects for themselves and their families.

The more we understand the good and bad points of drugs and why we use them, the better we are able to make good decisions for ourselves rather than being pushed into risky behaviour by others.

• Activities

1 Make a map of your community. Draw small pictures or symbols of all the drugs, including alcohol and tobacco, that people use in your community and put them on the map, using the questions below.

Discuss each drug one by one, using the following questions:

- Where is each drug grown, produced or sold?
- Where do different people obtain and use the drug?
- Where do people first start to use the drug?
- When do they use it most?

2 Make flow charts for each drug showing the good and the bad points of each for individuals, families and communities.

3 Look for ways to avoid the bad points and benefit from the good points.

Points of view

Here are the views of some young people on alcohol, smoking and drugs.

'I think older people get rich from selling drugs like cannabis. Then the boys smoke too much and they rape the girls. Young people are blamed for using drugs but it's our elders who sell them to us.'

'When people tell us to stop taking drugs, they always forget that we take them because we like the feeling they give us. Life is difficult and to feel free from our problems for a short time must be good.'

We are going to look now at something that does make us healthy – food! The food that we eat has a big effect on our health.

You are what you eat

Young people, both boys and girls, are growing fast and using a lot of energy. They are making bone and muscles, blood and organs. For all this growth and energy you need to eat a large enough amount of a mixture of foods. Food is also needed for protection against diseases and for intellectual development. Choose mixtures of the cheapest locally available cereals or roots, green leafy vegetables and beans, groundnuts or oilseeds.

Activities

1 Gather together all the foods that you can find in your community or draw pictures of them. Now sort the foods into piles according to your ideas about what they do in the body.

- Which foods give you **energy**?
- Which foods help you to **grow**?
- Which foods **protect you from sickness and make blood and bones**?

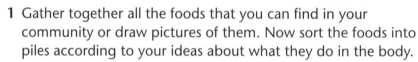

Sort the foods in other ways, for example, in terms of cost, how easy it is to prepare or cook them, whether they are plentiful from the farm or market, how long they satisfy hunger, taste etc.

HIGH ENERGY FOODS

2 Make a seasonal calendar to show which foods are around at different times of the year.

ENERGY FOODS

3 Design meals that could give you all the nutrients you need throughout the year. Do you need to grow some additional foods in some seasons?

4 Keep a diary showing all the foods you ate over the past week.

- What are the differences between the boys' and girls' food diaries?

- Do boys and girls have breakfast before they go to school? Are they able to eat something at midday? Are girls pushed into relationships with men or boys to get something to eat for lunch?

- Are there foods that girls are not allowed to eat? Why is this?

DY BUILDING FOOD

Why do girls need to eat well?

The bones in the pelvis need to grow well so that there is enough room for the baby to pass through during childbirth. Girls who don't eat enough may have very narrow pelvises so that the baby cannot get out. This is serious because mother and baby can die or the mother can tear herself. Calcium helps the bones to grow well and the hips to become wide for safe childbirth. Calcium is found in milk, curd, yoghurt, green leafy vegetables, beans, shell fish, ground sesame or melon seeds and the liquid from egg shells or bones soaked in lemon or lime juice for a few hours.

FOOD FOR PROTECTION

Girls lose blood during their monthly periods and they need to replace this blood by eating foods containing iron and protein. If they do not do this, the blood becomes very pale. This is called anaemia and is dangerous particularly during the malaria season. Foods containing iron are dark green leafy vegetables, liver and red meat, beans, groundnuts, melon seeds, eggs and foods containing yeast such as porridge made from fermented sorghum before it turns to beer.

Here is your lunch money. Do buy peanuts or bananas from it rather than coca-cola.

If you are buying snacks from food vendors outside school, try to choose a nutritious one. For example, banana and groundnuts; dishes made from beans; bread and peanut butter; peanut cakes (kulikuli) help you to grow better than highly processed foods like crisps or chocolate. It is better to spend your money on freshly cooked foods than on Coke.

We have seen that what we eat is important for our health. In the next section, we look at exercise, another important part of staying healthy.

Exercise

A certain amount of physical activity helps the body to be strong, flexible and have a good heart and lungs. Exercise that makes us pant is good for the heart and lungs. However, carrying heavy loads on the head or back and bending down for long hours can put too much stress on the body and cause pain and fatigue.

Exercise can help to prevent stress.

● Activity

In groups of girls only and boys only, make a weekly routine chart to show what types of exercise you take on each day of the week. Share your diagrams and discuss them.

Many young people, especially girls, who live in rural areas do a lot of exercise every day in their routine life. On the other hand, young people living in urban areas may find it more difficult to take exercise unless they do sport. If some people do not take some vigorous exercise every day, try to understand the reasons, and find ways to help them.

Rest

It is important to get enough rest. Young people often feel very tired when they are growing fast and this is probably the body's way of getting enough rest.

Use your daily routine charts to count how many hours of sleep and relaxation you get every day.

- Is there a difference between boys and girls?

Often girls and women work longer hours than boys and men because they do both farming or money-earning tasks and household tasks. Is there a way that the workloads of boys and girls can be made more equal so that girls have more rest?

Overwork is one of the causes of stress in our lives and we look at this further in the next section.

Coping with stress

Ama's story

Ama's mother has AIDS and her father has gone away. Ama is responsible for caring for her four brothers and sisters and helping her mother. She hopes to go on to secondary school. It is the farming season. The children helped her to plant and now the weeds are growing fast. The food in the granary is almost finished and the price of food is increasing. The rains have brought malaria and her little sister has fever. It is the time for exams and paying fees. If she doesn't pay her fees, she will be thrown out. Ama wakes in the night and thinks about all her problems. Her heart beats fast and she shakes. Sometimes she has nightmares that her mother is dead and they have no food or money and the children are hungry. She finds herself shouting at the little ones and slapping them. They are shocked. Why is their sister behaving like this?

Ama is suffering from stress. She feels afraid because she cannot see how she can cope with all the family problems. Many young people have difficult lives because of poverty, school work or difficult family situations. They feel very stressed and if this goes on for a long time, it can make them feel that life is not worth living. Too much stress affects your body and your mind.

1 Work in small groups and think of all the things that make you stressed. Rank them to see which are the most important causes of stress.

2 Now take some important causes of stress and try to see whether there is anything you can do to reduce these causes.

3 Sometimes, you may have no control over the causes of your stress. But you may be able to reduce the level of stress they cause you. Share ideas on how you might do this.

4 Share ideas about what you do to try to reduce stress in your lives.

5 Come together in a big group and put together all your ideas on how to reduce the causes and effects of stress.

6 If Ama was your friend, how would you try to help her? She has a very hard life. What can she do to reduce stress?

Ways you might be able to reduce stress

Pray to your God to share your load with you so that you do not worry so much about your problems.

Talk about your problems with someone you trust. Have a good cry – it can relieve stress and sadness. If your friends or neighbours have similar problems, meet together and share your worries and feelings. Look for solutions that you could act on together.

Laughter and play are good ways of reducing stress; don't stop playing because you are growing up; enjoy childish games with your siblings.

Relaxation helps to reduce stress. Close your eyes and breathe slowly, focusing on the breath going in and out of your body. Now start from your left foot and relax all the bones and muscles in it. Move up to your calf muscle and so on until you have relaxed your whole body.

Do something that you enjoy, maybe dancing or singing or reading at least once every day.

Uncle, I would be grateful if you could help me with…

Find something beautiful to focus your mind on – maybe a flower or a candle or the sea or a piece of music or a peaceful place or special person. Try to empty your mind of everything else but the thing you are focusing on. If you do this for some time each day, it will help you to relax.

Don't carry all your problems on your own shoulders. Try to see how others can help you in your home and outside. Maybe your brothers or sisters can do some of your tasks; can a relative or an organisation help you with some problems? Rank your problems and set goals to solve one or two of the most serious problems soon.

If a young person is showing serious signs of stress, depression or anxiety, it is best if she or he can see a health worker or doctor for help.

Coping with sadness

Things happen in all our lives that make us feel sad. People we love die or leave us. We fail exams or do not get the job we wanted. Our harvests fail and drought dries up all our wells. We experience violence and abuse. Sadness is a normal part of life. Deep sadness that goes on for more than a short time is called 'depression'.

Depression may be caused by losses in our lives. People can feel depressed because of chemical changes in their bodies. For example, girls may feel sad before their periods. Some illegal drugs make you feel very happy at first but when they stop, you feel very sad. When people suffer from bad depression, it may be an illness that several family members suffer from.

How do you know if someone is depressed?

A depressed person may feel or do any of the following:

- often feel very sad and cry a lot;
- lose all interest in life, friends and family, school, work and him or herself;
- feel that they are no good at anything;
- have trouble sleeping and no energy; feel irritable;
- eat too much or too little;
- try to commit suicide;
- feel unhappy to be alive or guilty that they are alive whilst someone else is dead.

1 Think to yourself about what you do to make yourself feel happier when you are sad. Share your ideas with friends in a small group.

2 Think about how you can help a friend or family member who is sad. Share these ideas with a small group.

3 Draw pictures to show all the people in and outside the community who might help someone who is very sad or stressed. Place the pictures on the floor with the most important people in the middle and the less important people further away.

Sometimes health workers prescribe drugs called tranquillisers to treat depression and stress. These can help if properly prescribed. These pills may be freely on sale in the market. Tranquillisers may make you feel better at first but it is very easy to become addicted to them. It then becomes difficult to stop taking them.

A person who is very depressed needs help from a qualified person. There may be traditional healers who can treat depression or use tranquillising herbs that are not addictive.

Talking to friends or a trusted relative or helper may cheer you up. Having a treat, focusing your mind on good things that have happened, can help to lift your sadness. Sometimes you just want to be alone and feel sad or cry. This is better than trying to put on a brave face and cheerful mask when you are feeling miserable.

We have come to the end of the chapter on 'Keeping ourselves healthy'. We hope that it has given you some ideas about ways in which you can look after yourselves and each other so that you enjoy an active and happy life.

9 | Working together for a better world

In this chapter, we discuss our hopes and look for ways to achieve them. We plan how to link hands with our family, friends and neighbours, professionals and leaders to make the world we live in a safer and happier place.

Singing a rainbow

If you had a whole hour to yourself, what would you do to make yourself happy?

We all have different things that make us feel content or happy. Probably many of them fit into one of the seven ideas shown in the picture of the rainbow. These ideas are relationships, self-esteem, things I am good at, giving, fun, things I value and inspiration.

• Activities

1 Make a big rainbow on the ground. Put different coloured flowers, leaves or other objects on each arch of the rainbow to show its colour. For example, you might use a yellow flower to show the yellow arch of the rainbow. Make a picture or symbols to show the idea for each colour. Take each colour of the rainbow one by one and draw pictures or role-play examples of that idea which make you happy. Why does this make you happy?

2 In pairs, talk about the barriers that make it difficult for you to do the things that make you happy and the things that help you. How could you lower or remove these barriers?

3 Make a plan with your friend to do one thing that makes you happy today.

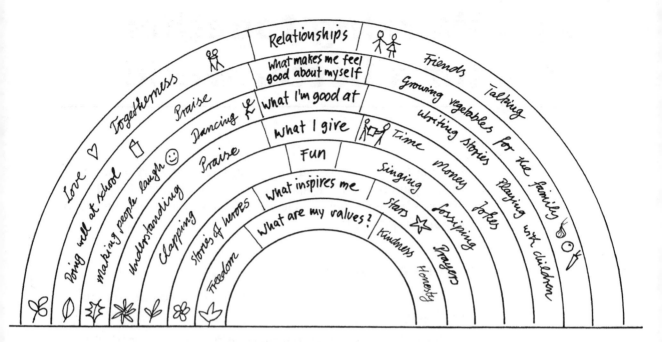

The rainbow diagram contains the following words, from left to right and outer to inner:

Love, Togetherness, Praise
Doing well at school, making people laugh, Dancing
Understanding, Clapping, Praise
Stories of heroes, Freedom

Relationships
What makes me feel good about myself
What I'm good at
What I give
Fun
What inspires me
What are my values?

Friends, Talking
Growing vegetables for the family, Writing stories, Playing with children
Time, Money, Jokes
Singing, Worshipping, Prayers
Stars, Kindness, Honesty

Getting help when we need it

Each of us at times gives help to others. Each of us has difficult times when we need help. Receiving and giving help is part of life. Sometimes we find it difficult to ask for help when we need it because we are feeling low and uncertain. It is best to think about people whom we can ask for help **before** a problem occurs so that we can ask for help quickly. We can build up networks of people who can help us and whom we can help. It is strong, not weak, to ask for help when we need it.

We can get help from ourselves, people close to us and 'experts'. Each type of help is important. People have different qualities and skills so that they can give us different types of help.

Find a ball of wool or string. Sit in a circle, with one person holding the ball of wool. This person then says one quality that she or he has for helping others and throws the ball to someone else, holding on to a piece of the wool. Repeat until everyone has caught the ball and said a helping quality. The web you have made links you all and holds you up.

Family members can help us with different problems. Probably each of them can help in a different way. Our friends and lovers can also help.

● Activities

1 Make a picture of balloons to show all the people close to you who can help you. Make bigger balloons for people who are very important and smaller balloons for less important people. If you see the person often put them close to you. If you see them rarely put the balloon far away. Write helping qualities of each person on the balloon.

2 Make the same sort of 'balloon' picture for 'experts' who could help you with a particular problem, for example teachers, nurses, agricultural extension officers, priests or traditional counsellors. Make a map and put these experts on it. This will help people to find the 'experts' if they need them.

3 In small groups, make up a story about a young person who has a problem. Choose someone to role-play this person. Take it in turns to role-play the different close people or experts who could help this person with his or her problem.

Finding our haven

A haven is a place where we feel peaceful, safe, free, calm or renewed. It is a place where we can think, have fun, create, be ourselves. A haven can be a physical place like a quiet riverside or forest, a special tree or garden. A haven can also be a place in our minds where we can go whenever we wish for peace and freedom. This could be the memory of a beautiful place or special person or listening to music. A haven can help us to cope with problems and refresh our spirits.

Tell your friend about your havens. Could you create a haven nearby where you could go to feel good? Could you share this haven with your best friends?

Hopes

What does hope mean to you?

There are different kinds of hope. Some of our hopes are like dreams, we have little control over them. Winning the lottery is this kind of hope. Other hopes are goals that we can work to achieve. A girl might hope to become a business woman. She works hard at school to achieve this. A girl may hope to marry a rich, kind husband. She may take steps to achieve this, by making herself attractive, behaving well and choosing male company carefully. Some hopes are like a faith or belief. Some are challenges.

Why is hope important to us?

Hope can motivate us to continue through difficult times or to bear a crisis until it passes. This is very important to our well-being. Hope can give us a purpose in life, which leads to happiness and fulfilment.

We can learn to plan our achievements so that they can help us reach our hopes.

● Activities

1 Invite each person to think of one hope that they want to achieve.

Draw a star shape and put the hope in the middle. Then think of ways to make your hope achievable. Answer the following questions and put them at the point of each star:

- Is your hope clear?
- Is it realistic?
- Is it achievable?
- When can you achieve it?
- How will you know when you reach it?

How will I know when I reach it?

When?

Is it clear?

Is it realistic?

Can I achieve it?

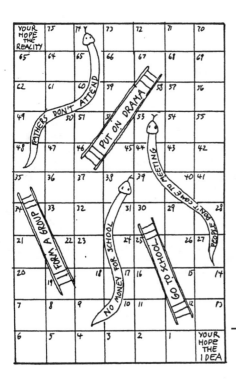

2 Make a game of snakes and ladders. Put your hope in the last square – this is what you are trying to reach. You can play this game individually or in small groups. If you are in a group, you need to agree on your hope. On each ladder, put something that will help you to achieve your hope. On each snake, put a barrier to reaching your hope. Now play the game. Each time you go up a ladder, stop to think about how you can make this ladder in your life. For each snake, discuss what will help you to overcome the barrier.

Our Story

One of our ladders was to form a group of girls. We wanted to have fun together, help each other with problems, share our skills and request help from outside to improve our lives. So we elected our leaders and arranged a time to meet every week. We sang and danced with drums until we got so good that we could earn money. Those of us who could read taught our friends who had not been to school. We reared animals and grew vegetables together, sharing our profit between the group and ourselves. This group has really helped us to climb the ladder to our hopes of a better life.

One of our snakes was the harassment by older men who offered us presents for sex. We needed the money but so often it led to pregnancy and AIDS and they refused to use condoms. Once we started our group we decided to help each other avoid these men. We practised saying 'no' and put on a drama requesting them to stop their harassment.

After identifying what helps and what stops you from achieving your hope, plan the next steps, using the planning questions on page 122.

Planning questions

- What are we going to do?
- Why are we doing it?
- Who will do it with us?
- Who will it benefit?
- When will we do it?
- How will we do it?
- Where will we do it?
- What money, materials and people will we need to help us?
- What will the result be?

Sharing this book with your friends

The knowledge you have gained from this book can help other young people who have not read it or used it with their friends.

Activities

1 Brainstorm to think of as many ways as possible in which you can share your knowledge with your friends, especially those who do not go to school or cannot read and write. For example, you could form an adolescent club or share your knowledge through your church or mosque – what ideas can you think of?

2 List all the ideas and discuss the good and bad points about each. Agree on ways in which you will share what you have learnt individually and as a group.

Go for it!

You have now reached the end of this book. We hope you have enjoyed reading it and doing the activities. Now it is over to you to carry on using what you have learnt and helping your friends.

• Activities

1 Individually, think about these questions:

- What are the most important things that I have gained by using this book?
- What promises will I make to myself about using what I have gained in my life?

2 Make pictures or write down words to remind yourself of your promises. Keep the paper in a safe place so you can see how you are doing from time to time.

This world is not an easy place to live in. Problems like poverty and AIDS make life very hard for many people. But if we work together and help each other we are in a stronger position to make things better for ourselves and our children. We know that the support of a loving family and friends helps people to stay healthy and happy. Even if our family members are scattered or no longer with us, we can form close friendships so that we are not alone. Together we can work to improve our homes, surroundings and society so that we can reach our full abilities as capable and caring human beings.

The world is changing but we do not need to be afraid because if we work together we can achieve our hopes and dreams of a better tomorrow.

Using the activities

The following suggestions aim to help young people and those working with them to do the activities in a safe, enjoyable and effective way.

Working with groups

- Try not to have more than 15 people in one group. Divide into smaller groups or pairs to discuss sensitive topics.

- Start with groups of the same sex, especially for sensitive topics. When people have gained confidence, mix boys and girls together to share their ideas and get used to talking to each other on these issues. Find ways that young and older people can share their ideas.

- Do the activities in a place where people feel comfortable, private and free from interruptions.

- Arrange the seating so that everyone feels a part of the group, able to make eye contact with everyone and to talk and hear easily. For example, sit in a circle without desks.

- Explain that in this book people learn through discussions and activities, rather than lectures. Each person has valuable ideas and people should feel free to express their ideas and feelings.

- Say that we all feel embarrassed at times when talking about sexual matters. But talking is essential if we are to enjoy safe and happy lives. Point out that because a person talks about sex does not mean that they are unusually free in their behaviour.

- Use games such as singing and dancing to help people to relax at the start of an activity or after a difficult topic.

- Agree on some ground rules with the group.

Our ground rules

1 We will not talk about personal stories and ideas that are discussed in the group to people outside the group.

2 We will speak one at a time and listen to each other. Let's begin by going round the group and giving everyone a chance to speak.

3 We will help noisy people to quieten down and quiet people to speak.

4 We each have a right not to participate. We will never pressure anyone to take part in an activity or share personal information.

5 We will respect each other's right to our own opinions and values. We won't judge or ridicule people.

6 We will take responsibility for challenging harmful prejudice and oppression in ourselves and others.

7 We all have a right to change our minds and make mistakes.

8 No question is stupid or not worth asking.

- Ask open-ended, probing and clarifying questions to encourage people to talk more fully.

- Put a box in the room so that people can write their questions anonymously.

- Focus the discussion and summarise so that people can see what they have covered and where to go next.

- If you are using a story, agony aunt letter, role play or picture to start a discussion, use these questions:

  What is happening in the story or picture?

  Does this happen to people like us?

What are the causes and consequences of the situation?

How could the characters solve the problem or what could the characters have done to avoid the problems?

Role plays

In a role play, people act out a particular situation. They may act as themselves or play the role of another person. There is no written script in role play and the focus is on what happens in the interaction, not how well people 'perform' or act.

Role play is used as a basis for discussion; to increase communication skills and self-esteem; to explore different situations and ways of dealing with them; to express feelings openly and see how others feel; to get inside other people's shoes and to rehearse for the future.

How to use role play

Involve everyone as participants with a role or observers. Ask people to volunteer for roles. Start in pairs or small groups with a few observers to build confidence. Encourage people to get into the role they are playing. If they are playing a new character, have people asking them questions about themselves to help them get into that person's shoes. If they are playing themselves in a new situation, they should respond as honestly as possible to that situation.

Help the role players to stay focused and explore the situation fully. Most role plays come to a natural pause. The best role plays are fairly short, not more than ten minutes at the most.

Tell the observers what to look for in the role play by giving them some questions. For example:

- What happened?
- Why did it happen?
- What did the characters feel?
- How did others react?

After the role play, give each of the players an opportunity to express their feelings about the characters and situations they portrayed. Then ask them to shed their characters and return to themselves by removing any props, saying their names and something about themselves.

Then discuss what everyone learnt from the experience, analyse the role play and discuss its relevance to their lives.

Talk about the role play positively in ways that increase the self-esteem of the players, especially if they have been brave enough to practise new skills and deal with a difficult situation. Give praise first before suggestions for improvement. Help with information and skills as necessary.

Hot-seating

In hot-seating, the players stay in role after the play. The observers ask them questions to deepen understanding of their motives, feelings and situation. The observers can challenge them by asking why they behaved as they did, but they should not judge them.

Forum theatre

In forum theatre, the role play is shown once. It is then replayed from the beginning. The observers can clap and say 'freeze' to stop the play at any point. They then 'go into the shoes of' one of the characters and change what they say and/or do so that the situation goes better. The observers then discuss whether the new way worked well and whether it is realistic. The play then continues from where it was before the freeze.

Tableau

A tableau is a statue or still picture that quickly and actively depicts the thoughts and feelings of participants without words or movement. The statues are made by individuals, pairs, small or large groups in response to a word or a theme, for example, anger or relationships. People can make themselves into the statue or one person can sculpt others by placing their body and limbs in a certain position or showing them what to do. The observers look carefully at the statue and say what they think it means. They can then ask the players to tell them more about what is happening.

Stories

You might use the stories in the book in different ways. For example, read the story aloud and then discuss it or role-play the story or draw pictures of the different scenes. You might tell the story in the way that it is written and then re-tell it so that the characters avoid the problems and have a happier life.

Reading and writing

People who cannot read and write can do many of the activities in this book, for example, role play, story-telling and drawing. However, some of the activities do suggest that people read or write. If you are working with a group where all or some people cannot read and write, adapt the activity so that they are able to take part. For example, they might draw pictures or use objects as symbols to depict an idea. If some people can write, you might use this as an opportunity to increase literacy skills in those who find it difficult.

Drawings and diagrams

Try drawing and making some of the diagrams shown in the book, for example, flow charts, maps and seasonal calendars. These methods are called Participatory Learning and Action (PLA) because they help people to share and add to their knowledge, to analyse their situation, to plan and to act. Everyone can draw on the ground with a stick, on the blackboard or walls with chalk or on paper. The drawing does not have to be professional because the artist can explain what it means. Help everyone in the group to pick up the pen or stick and add their ideas. Use leaves, flowers, seeds, stones or sticks to mark different places on the map or diagram, or to score. If you draw on the ground, record it on paper to refer to later.

Quizzes

Read out the questions in the quiz one by one and discuss the answers in small groups. Or ask everyone to write down their own answers and add up their scores before discussing the questions. If people cannot write, use beans or stones to score. People should enjoy the quizzes as fun, not see them as a test. The discussion about the questions is as important as the answers. People can share and get information through the quiz.

Visits to health and other services

It is very helpful to visit local services in a group and talk with the service providers. If you have an opportunity to ask questions and express your concerns, you will feel more confident to use the services. Involve the whole community in the use of the book so that you get the support you need.

Talking with people in the community

Some activities suggest that you talk with people in the community. For example, talk with grandmothers about how gender relations have changed since their day. You can make this go well by involving the community in the activities and trying to get agreement on the needs of young people for sexual and reproductive health education.

Points of view

Take it in turns to read each of the points of view and empathise with the characters followed by discussion. Each person might take one of the people with a point of view and get into that role. The group could then have a discussion with people staying in their roles.